A2-Level
Chemistry

A2 Chemistry is seriously tricky — no question about that.
To do well, you're going to need to revise properly and practise hard.

This book has thorough notes on all the theory you need,
and it's got practice questions... lots of them.
For every topic there are warm-up and exam-style questions.

And of course, we've done our best to make the whole thing vaguely entertaining for you.

Complete Revision and Practice
Exam Board: AQA

Editors:

Amy Boutal, Mary Falkner, Sharon Keeley, Simon Little, Michael Southorn, Julie Wakeling.

Contributors:

Mike Bossart, Rob Clarke, Ian H. Davis, John Duffy, Lucy Muncaster, Jane Simoni,
Paul Warren, Chris Workman.

Proofreaders:

Barrie Crowther, Paul Jordin, Julie Wakeling.

Published by CGP

ISBN: 978 1 84762 261 7

With thanks to Laura Stoney for the copyright research.

Groovy website: www.cgpbooks.co.uk
Jolly bits of clipart from CorelDRAW®
Printed by Elanders Ltd, Newcastle upon Tyne.

Based on the classic CGP style created by Richard Parsons.

Contents

How Science Works

The Scientific Process 2

Unit 4: Section 1 — Kinetics and Equilibria

Rate Equations 4
More on Rates and Rate Equations 6
The Equilibrium Constant 8
Acids, Bases and pH 11
More pH Calculations 14
pH Curves, Titrations and Indicators 16
Titration Calculations 18
Buffer Action 20

Unit 4: Section 2 — Basic Organic Chemistry & Isomerism

Naming Organic Compounds 22
Formulas and Isomers 24
Optical Isomerism 26

Unit 4: Section 3 — Carbonyl Compounds

Aldehydes and Ketones 28
Carboxylic Acids and Esters 30
More on Esters 32
Acyl Chlorides 34

Unit 4: Section 4 — More Organic Chemistry

Aromatic Compounds 36
Amines Mainly 39
Amino Acids and Proteins 42
Polymers 44
More on Polymers 46

Unit 4: Section 5 — Synthesis and Analysis

Organic Synthesis and Analysis 48
Mass Spectrometry 51
NMR Spectroscopy 54
More About NMR 56
IR Spectroscopy and Chromatography 58

Unit 5: Section 1 — Thermodynamics

Lattice Enthalpies 61
Enthalpies of Solution 64
Entropy Change 66
Free-Energy Change 68

Unit 5: Section 2 — Period 3 and Redox Equilibria

Period 3 Elements and Oxides 70
Redox Equations 72
Electrode Potentials 74
Electrochemical Series 76
Electrochemical Cells 78

Unit 5: Section 3 — Transition Metals

Transition Metals — The Basics 80
Complex Ions 82
Formation of Coloured Ions 84
Variable Oxidation States 86
Titrations with Transition Metals 88
Uses of Transition Metals 90

Unit 5: Section 4 — Inorganic Reactions

Metal-Aqua Ions 93
Substitution Reactions 96

Practical and Investigative Skills 98

Answers 101

Index 109

The Scientific Process

'How Science Works' is all about the scientific process — how we develop and test scientific ideas.
It's what scientists do all day, every day (well except at coffee time — never come between scientists and their coffee).

Scientists Come Up with Theories — Then Test Them...

Science tries to explain **how** and **why** things happen. It's all about seeking and gaining **knowledge** about the world around us. Scientists do this by **asking** questions and **suggesting** answers and then **testing** them, to see if they're correct — this is the **scientific process**.

1) **Ask** a question — make an **observation** and ask **why or how** whatever you've observed happens.
   E.g. Why does sodium chloride dissolve in water?

2) **Suggest** an answer, or part of an answer, by forming a **theory** or a **model** (a possible **explanation** of the observations or a description of what you think is actually happening).
   E.g. Sodium chloride is made up of charged particles, which are pulled apart by the polar water molecules.

3) Make a **prediction** or **hypothesis** — a **specific testable statement**, based on the theory, about what will happen in a test situation.
   E.g. A solution of sodium chloride will conduct electricity much better than water does.

4) Carry out **tests** — to provide **evidence** that will support the prediction or refute it.
   E.g. Measure the conductivity of water and of sodium chloride solution.

The evidence supported Quentin's Theory of Flammable Burps.

A theory is only scientific if it can be tested.

...Then They Tell Everyone About Their Results...

The results are **published** — scientists need to let others know about their work. Scientists publish their results in **scientific journals**. These are just like normal magazines, only they contain **scientific reports** (called papers) instead of the latest celebrity gossip.

1) Scientific reports are similar to the **lab write-ups** you do in school. And just as a lab write-up is **reviewed** (marked) by your teacher, reports in scientific journals undergo **peer review** before they're published.

   Scientists use standard terminology when writing their reports. This way they know that other scientists will understand them. For instance, there are internationally agreed rules for naming organic compounds, so that scientists across the world will know exactly what substance is being referred to.

2) The report is sent out to **peers** — other scientists who are experts in the **same area**. They go through it bit by bit, examining the methods and data, and checking it's all clear and logical. When the report is approved, it's **published**. This makes sure that work published in scientific journals is of a **good standard**.

3) But peer review **can't guarantee** the science is **correct** — other scientists still need to **reproduce** it.

4) Sometimes **mistakes** are made and bad work is published. Peer review **isn't perfect** but it's probably the best way for scientists to self-regulate their work and to publish **quality reports**.

...Then Other Scientists Will Test the Theory Too

1) Other scientists read the published theories and results, and try to **test the theory** themselves. This involves:
   • Repeating the **exact same experiments**.
   • Using the theory to make **new predictions** and then testing them with **new experiments**.

2) If all the experiments in the world provide evidence to back it up, the theory is thought of as **scientific 'fact'** (for now).

3) If **new evidence** comes to light that **conflicts** with the current evidence the theory is questioned all over again. More rounds of **testing** will be carried out to try to find out where the theory **falls down**.

This is how the **scientific process works** — **evidence** supports a theory, loads of other scientists read it and test it for themselves, eventually all the scientists in the world **agree** with it and then bingo, you get to **learn** it.

This is exactly how scientists arrived at the structure of the atom — and how they came to
the conclusion that electrons are arranged in shells and orbitals. It took years and years
for these models to be developed and accepted — this is often the case with the scientific process.

The Scientific Process

If the **Evidence** Supports a Theory, It's **Accepted** — for Now

Our currently accepted theories have survived this '**trial by evidence**'. They've been tested **over and over again** and each time the results have backed them up. **BUT**, and this is a big but (teehee), they never become totally indisputable fact. Scientific **breakthroughs or advances** could provide new ways to question and test the theory, which could lead to **changes and challenges** to it. Then the testing starts all over again...

And this, my friend, is the **tentative nature of scientific knowledge** — it's always **changing** and **evolving**.

When CFCs were first used in fridges in the 1930s, scientists thought they were problem-free — well, why not? There was no evidence to say otherwise. It was decades before anyone found out that CFCs were actually making a whopping great hole in the ozone layer.

Evidence Comes From **Lab Experiments**...

1) Results from **controlled experiments** in **laboratories** are **great**.

2) A lab is the easiest place to **control variables** so that they're all **kept constant** (except for the one you're investigating).

3) This means you can draw meaningful **conclusions**.

For example, if you're investigating how temperature affects the rate of a reaction you need to keep everything but the temperature constant, e.g. the pH of the solution, the concentration of the solution, etc.

...But You **Can't** Always do a Lab Experiment

There are things you **can't** study in a lab. And outside the lab controlling the variables is tricky, if not impossible.

- *Are increasing CO_2 emissions causing climate change?*
  There are other variables which may have an effect, such as changes in solar activity.
  You can't easily rule out every possibility. Also, climate change is a very **gradual process**.
  Scientists won't be able to tell if their predictions are correct for donkey's years.

- *Does drinking chlorinated tap water increase the risk of developing certain cancers?*
  There are always differences between groups of people. The best you can do is to
  have a **well-designed study** using **matched groups** — **choose two groups** of people
  (those who drink tap water and those who don't) which are **as similar as possible**
  (same mix of ages, same mix of diets etc.). But you still can't rule out every possibility.
  Taking newborn identical twins and treating them identically, except for making
  one drink gallons of tap water and the other only pure water, might be a fairer test,
  but it would present huge **ethical problems**.

Samantha thought her study was very well designed — especially the fitted bookshelf.

Science Helps to Inform Decision-Making

Lots of scientific work eventually leads to **important discoveries** that **could** benefit humankind — but there are often **risks** attached (and almost always **financial costs**).

Society (that's you, me and everyone else) must weigh up the information in order to **make decisions** — about the way we live, what we eat, what we drive, and so on. Information is also used by **politicians** to devise policies and laws.

- Scientific advances mean that **hydrogen-oxygen fuel cells** can now be made (see page 79). They're better for the **environment** than batteries, because their only waste product is **water**. But you do need to **use energy** to produce the **hydrogen** and **oxygen** in the first place. And hydrogen is **highly flammable**, so it's tricky to store safely.

- Pharmaceutical drugs are really expensive to develop, and drug companies want to make money. So they put most of their efforts into developing drugs that they can sell for a good price. Society has to consider the **cost** of buying new drugs — the **NHS** can't afford the most expensive drugs without **sacrificing** something else.

- **Synthetic polymers** are very useful — they're **cheap** to produce and very **durable**. But they're **hard to dispose of** (they don't break down easily). So we need to make choices about how we can best dispose of plastics (see page 46) and whether we should try to **reduce** the amount that we use, or work to develop more **biodegradable plastics**.

So there you have it — how science works...

Hopefully these pages have given you a nice intro to how science works, e.g. what scientists do to provide you with 'facts'. You need to understand this, as you're expected to know how science works yourselves — for the exam and for life.

Rate Equations

Sorry — this first section's a bit mathsy. Just take a deep breath, dive in, and don't bash your head on the bottom.

The **Reaction Rate** tells you How Fast **Reactants** are Converted to **Products**

The **reaction rate** is the **change in the amount** of reactants or products **per unit time** (normally per second).
If the reactants are in **solution**, the rate will be **change in concentration per second** and the units will be **$moldm^{-3}s^{-1}$**.

If you draw a graph of the **amount of reactant or product against time** for a reaction, the rate at any point is given by the **gradient** at that point on the graph. If the graph's a curve, you have to draw a **tangent** to the curve and find the gradient of that.

A tangent is a line that just touches a curve and has the same gradient as the curve does at that point.

A graph of the **concentration of a reactant against time** might look something like this:

Duncan always took care to label his axes.

At the start of the reaction the tangent is steepest — so the reaction's fastest here. This is the initial rate.

The rate decreases as the reaction goes on.

The reaction's finished here — so the gradient is zero.

The **Rate Equation** links **Reaction Rate** to **Reactant Concentrations**

Rate equations look ghastly, but all they're really telling you is how the **rate** is affected by the **concentrations of reactants**. For a general reaction: **A + B → C + D**, the **rate equation** is:

The units of rate are $moldm^{-3}s^{-1}$.

$$Rate = k[A]^m[B]^n$$

Remember — square brackets mean the concentration of whatever's inside them.

1) **m** and **n** are the **orders of the reaction** with respect to reactant A and reactant B.
   m tells you how the **concentration of reactant A** affects the **rate** and **n** tells you the same for **reactant B**.

> If [A] changes and the rate **stays the same**, the order of reaction with respect to A is **0**.
> *So if [A] doubles, the rate will stay the same. If [A] triples, the rate will stay the same.*
>
> If the rate is **proportional to [A]**, then the order of reaction with respect to A is **1**.
> *So if [A] doubles, the rate will double. If [A] triples, the rate will triple.*
>
> If the rate is **proportional to $[A]^2$**, then the order of reaction with respect to A is **2**.
> *So if [A] doubles, the rate will be 2^2 = 4 times faster. If [A] triples, the rate will be 3^2 = 9 times faster.*

2) The **overall order of the reaction** is **m + n**.

3) You can only find **orders of reaction** from **experiments**. You **can't** work them out from chemical equations.

4) **k** is the **rate constant** — the bigger it is, the **faster** the reaction. The rate constant is **always the same** for a certain reaction at a **particular temperature** — but if you **increase** the temperature, the rate constant rises too.

> When you **increase** the **temperature** of a reaction, the **rate of reaction increases** — you're increasing the **number of collisions** between reactant molecules, and also the **energy** of each collision. But the **concentrations** of the reactants and the **orders of reaction** stay the same. So the value of **k** must **increase** for the rate equation to balance.

> **Example:** The chemical equation below shows the acid-catalysed reaction between propanone and iodine.
>
> $$CH_3COCH_{3(aq)} + I_{2(aq)} \xrightarrow{H^+_{(aq)}} CH_3COCH_2I_{(aq)} + H^+_{(aq)} + I^-_{(aq)}$$
>
> This reaction is **first order** with respect to propanone and $H^+_{(aq)}$ and **zero order** with respect to iodine. Write down the rate equation for this reaction.
>
> *Even though $H^+_{(aq)}$ is a catalyst, rather than a reactant, it can still be in the rate equation.*
>
> The **rate equation** is: rate = $k[CH_3COCH_3]^1[H^+]^1[I_2]^0$
> But $[X]^1$ is usually written as $[X]$, and $[X]^0$ equals **1** so is usually **left out** of the rate equation.
> So you can **simplify** the rate equation to: **rate = $k[CH_3COCH_3][H^+]$**
>
> *Think about the indices laws from maths.*

Rate Equations

The **Initial Rates Method** can be used to work out **Rate Equations** too

The **initial rate of a reaction** is the rate right at the **start** of the reaction. You can find this from a **concentration-time** graph by calculating the **gradient** of the **tangent** at **time = 0**.

Initial rate = $\frac{y}{x}$

But you might get questions where they change more than one concentration, like the example below.

Here's a quick explanation of how to use the **initial rates method**:

1) Repeat the experiment several times using **different initial concentrations** of reactants. You should usually only change **one** of the concentrations at a time, keeping the rest constant.

2) Calculate the **initial rate** for each experiment using the method above.

3) Finally, see how the **initial concentrations** affect the **initial rates** and figure out the **order** for each reactant. The example below shows you how to do this. Once you know the **orders**, you can work out the rate equation.

Example:

The table on the right shows the results of a series of initial rate experiments for the reaction:

$$NO_{(g)} + CO_{(g)} + O_{2(g)} \rightarrow NO_{2(g)} + CO_{2(g)}$$

The experiments were carried out at a constant temperature.

Write down the rate equation for the reaction.

Experiment number	[NO] (moldm⁻³)	[CO] (moldm⁻³)	[O₂] (moldm⁻³)	Initial rate (moldm⁻³s⁻¹)
1	2.0×10^{-2}	1.0×10^{-2}	1.0×10^{-2}	0.17
2	6.0×10^{-2}	1.0×10^{-2}	1.0×10^{-2}	1.53
3	2.0×10^{-2}	2.0×10^{-2}	1.0×10^{-2}	0.17
4	4.0×10^{-2}	1.0×10^{-2}	2.0×10^{-2}	0.68

1) Look at experiments 1 and 2 — when [NO] **triples** (and all the other concentrations stay constant) the rate is **nine times** faster, and $9 = 3^2$. So the reaction is **second order** with respect to NO.

2) Look at experiments 1 and 3 — when **[CO]** doubles (but all the other concentrations stay constant), the rate **stays the same**. So the reaction is **zero order** with respect to CO.

3) Look at experiments 1 and 4 — the rate of experiment 4 is **four times faster** than experiment 1. The reaction is **second order** with respect to **[NO]**, so the rate will **quadruple** when you **double** [NO]. But in experiment 4, **[O₂]** has also been **doubled**. As doubling [O₂] hasn't had any additional effect on the rate, the reaction must be **zero order** with respect to O₂.

4) Now that you know the order with respect to each reactant you can write the rate equation: **rate = $k[NO]^2$** .

You can calculate k at this temperature by putting the concentrations and the initial rate from one of the experiments into the rate equation (see page 7).

Practice Questions

Q1 Explain what the term 'zero order' means.

Q2 How would the value of k change if you decreased the temperature of a chemical reaction?

Q3 Describe how you could find the initial rate of a reaction.

Exam Question

1   This table shows the results of a series of initial rate experiments for the reaction between substances D and E at a constant temperature:

Experiment	[D] (moldm⁻³)	[E] (moldm⁻³)	Initial rate × 10⁻³ (moldm⁻³s⁻¹)
1	0.2	0.2	1.30
2	0.2	0.4	2.60
3	0.1	0.1	0.65

a)   Find the orders of reaction with respect to reactants D and E. Explain your reasoning. [5 marks]

b)   Write the rate equation for the reaction in terms of k, the rate constant. [1 mark]

c)   The experiments were conducted at a temperature of 300 °C. State what will happen to the value of the rate constant, k, if the experiments are repeated at 500 °C. [1 mark]

Rate of A2 Chemistry Revision = k [Student] [Tea] ...

These rate equations might look a bit odd, but knowing how to use them can be really handy. Learn what all the different bits of the equation mean, and how to use it to find the overall order of reaction. And make sure that you understand the initial rates method, and that you can use it to work out orders of reaction — it's something examiners love to ask about.

More on Rates and Rate Equations

If you want to work out the mechanism of a reaction then you're going to have to know about the rate-determining step...

The **Rate-Determining Step** is the **Slowest Step** in a Multi-Step Reaction

Mechanisms can have **one step** or a **series of steps**. In a series of steps, each step can have a **different rate**. The **overall rate** is decided by the step with the **slowest** rate — the **rate-determining step**.

Otherwise known as the rate-limiting step.

Reactants in the **Rate Equation** Affect the **Rate**

The rate equation is handy for working out the **mechanism** of a chemical reaction. You need to be able to pick out which reactants from the chemical equation are involved in the **rate-determining step**:

If a reactant appears in the **rate equation**, it must affect the **rate**. So this reactant, or something derived from it, must be in the **rate-determining step**. If a reactant **doesn't** appear in the **rate equation**, then it **won't** be involved in the **rate-determining step** (and neither will anything derived from it).

Catalysts can appear in rate equations, so they can be in rate-determining steps too.

Some **important points** to remember about rate-determining steps and mechanisms are:
1) The rate-determining step **doesn't** have to be the first step in a mechanism.
2) The reaction mechanism **can't** usually be predicted from **just** the chemical equation.

Orders of Reaction Provide More Information About the **Rate-Determining Step**

The **order of a reaction** with respect to a reactant shows the **number of molecules** of that reactant that are involved in the **rate-determining step**.

So, if a reaction's second order with respect to X, there'll be two molecules of X in the rate-determining step.

For example, the mechanism for the reaction between **chlorine free radicals** and **ozone**, O_3, consists of **two steps**:

$$Cl\bullet_{(g)} + O_{3(g)} \rightarrow ClO\bullet_{(g)} + O_{2(g)} \text{ — slow (rate-determining step)}$$
$$ClO\bullet_{(g)} + O\bullet_{(g)} \rightarrow Cl\bullet_{(g)} + O_{2(g)} \text{ — fast}$$

$Cl\bullet$ and O_3 must both be in the rate equation, so the rate equation will be: **rate** $= k[Cl\bullet]^m[O_3]^n$. There's only **one** $Cl\bullet$ molecule and **one** O_3 molecule in the rate-determining step, so the **orders**, m and n, are both **1**. So the rate equation is **rate** $= k[Cl\bullet][O_3]$.

The **Rate-Determining Step** Can Help You Work Out the **Reaction Mechanism**

If you know which reactants are in the **rate-determining step**, you can work out the reaction **mechanism**.

There are two possible mechanisms for the nucleophile **OH⁻** substituting for **Br** in 2-bromo-2-methylpropane:

$$CH_3\text{-}\underset{\underset{CH_3}{|}}{\overset{\overset{CH_3}{|}}{C}}\text{-}Br + OH^- \rightarrow CH_3\text{-}\underset{\underset{CH_3}{|}}{\overset{\overset{CH_3}{|}}{C}}\text{-}OH + Br^-$$

or

$$CH_3\text{-}\underset{\underset{CH_3}{|}}{\overset{\overset{CH_3}{|}}{C}}\text{-}Br \rightarrow CH_3\text{-}\underset{\underset{CH_3}{|}}{\overset{\overset{CH_3}{|}}{C^+}} + Br^- \text{ — slow (rate-determining step)}$$
$$CH_3\text{-}\underset{\underset{CH_3}{|}}{\overset{\overset{CH_3}{|}}{C^+}} + OH^- \rightarrow CH_3\text{-}\underset{\underset{CH_3}{|}}{\overset{\overset{CH_3}{|}}{C}}\text{-}OH \text{ — fast}$$

The actual **rate equation** was worked out using rate experiments. It is: **rate** $= k[(CH_3)_3CBr]$
OH⁻ isn't in the **rate equation**, so it **can't** be involved in the rate-determining step. The **second mechanism** is correct because OH⁻ **isn't** in the rate-determining step.

Nitrogen monoxide can react with **oxygen** to produce **nitrogen dioxide**: $2NO + O_2 \rightarrow 2NO_2$
The rate equation for this reaction is: **rate** $= k[NO]^2[O_2]$.
So you know that the **rate-determining step** must involve **2 molecules of NO** and **1 molecule of O_2**.

The reaction **mechanism** for this reaction is made up of **two steps**:

Step 1 — $NO + NO \rightarrow N_2O_2$
Step 2 — $N_2O_2 + O_2 \rightarrow 2NO_2$

Neither step 1 nor step 2 contains all the molecules you'd expect from the rate equation. But in step 2 there's an **intermediate** molecule, N_2O_2, that's **derived from** 2 molecules of NO. So step 2 is the rate-determining step.

More on Rates and Rate Equations

Leaving reaction mechanisms behind for a moment, and getting back to rate equations...

You can Calculate the **Rate Constant** from the **Orders** and **Rate of Reaction**

Once the rate and the orders of the reaction have been found by experiment, you can work out the **rate constant**, k. The **units of k vary**, so you'll need to work them out too.

> **Example:** The reaction below is second order with respect to NO and zero order with respect to CO and O_2.
> At a certain temperature, the rate is 1.76×10^{-3} moldm^{-3}s^{-1}, when $[NO_{(g)}] = [CO_{(g)}] = [O_{2(g)}] = 2.00 \times 10^{-3}$ moldm^{-3}.
> Find the value of the rate constant, k, at this temperature.
>
> $$NO_{(g)} + CO_{(g)} + O_{2(g)} \rightarrow NO_{2(g)} + CO_{2(g)}$$
>
> First write out the **rate equation**:   Rate $= k[NO]^2[CO]^0[O_2]^0 = k[NO]^2$
>
> Next insert the **concentration** and the **rate**. **Rearrange** the equation and calculate the value of k:
>
> Rate $= k[NO]^2$, so, $1.76 \times 10^{-3} = k \times (2.00 \times 10^{-3})^2 \Rightarrow k = \dfrac{1.76 \times 10^{-3}}{(2.00 \times 10^{-3})^2} = 440$
>
> Find the **units of k** by putting the other units in the rate equation:
>
> Rate $= k[NO]^2$, so moldm^{-3}s^{-1} $= k \times$ (moldm^{-3})$^2 \Rightarrow k = \dfrac{\text{moldm}^{-3}\text{s}^{-1}}{(\text{moldm}^{-3})^2} = \dfrac{\text{s}^{-1}}{\text{moldm}^{-3}} = $ dm^{3}mol^{-1}s^{-1}
>
> So the answer is: k = 440 dm^{3}mol^{-1}s^{-1}

Practice Questions

Q1 What is meant by the 'rate-determining step' of a reaction?

Q2 Explain how knowing the rate equation for a reaction can help you to predict a reaction mechanism.

Q3 For a reaction between three reactants, X, Y and Z, the rate-determining step is $X + 2Y \rightarrow M + N$.
What will the order of reaction be with respect to :   a) reactant X?   b) reactant Y?   c) reactant Z?

Exam Questions

1   For the reaction $CH_3COOH_{(aq)} + C_2H_5OH_{(aq)} \rightarrow CH_3COOC_2H_{5(aq)} + H_2O_{(l)}$, the rate equation is Rate $= k[CH_3COOH][H^+]$.

What can you deduce about the role that H^+ plays in the reaction? Explain your answer.   [3 marks]

2   The following reaction is first order with respect to H_2 and first order with respect to ICl.

$$H_{2(g)} + 2ICl_{(g)} \rightarrow I_{2(g)} + 2HCl_{(g)}$$

a)   Write the rate equation for this reaction in terms of k, the rate constant.   [1 mark]

b)   The mechanism for this reaction consists of two steps.
   (i) Identify the molecules that are in the rate-determining step. Justify your answer.   [3 marks]
   (ii) A chemist suggested the following mechanism for the reaction:

$$2ICl_{(g)} \rightarrow I_{2(g)} + Cl_{2(g)} \quad\quad \text{slow}$$
$$H_{2(g)} + Cl_{2(g)} \rightarrow 2HCl_{(g)} \quad\quad \text{fast}$$

   Suggest, with reasons, whether this mechanism is likely to be correct.   [2 marks]

3   The following reaction is second order with respect to NO and first order with respect to H_2.

$$2NO_{(g)} + 2H_{2(g)} \rightarrow 2H_2O_{(g)} + N_{2(g)}$$

a)   Write a rate equation for the reaction in terms of k, the rate constant.   [1 mark]

b)   The rate of the reaction at 800 °C was determined to be 0.00267 moldm^{-3}s^{-1}
   when $[H_2] = 0.0020$ moldm^{-3} and $[NO] = 0.0040$ moldm^{-3}.
   (i) Calculate a value for the rate constant at 800 °C, including units.   [3 marks]
   (ii) Predict the effect on the rate constant of decreasing the temperature of the reaction to 600 °C.   [1 mark]

I found rate-determining step aerobics a bit on the slow side...

These pages show you how rate equations, orders of reaction, and reaction mechanisms all tie together and how each actually means something in the grand scheme of A2 Chemistry. It's all very profound. So get it all learnt and answer the questions and then you'll have plenty of time to practise the quickstep for your Strictly Come Dancing routine.

The Equilibrium Constant

There's a lot of toing and froing coming up. You won't know whether you're coming or going.

At **Equilibrium** the Amounts of Reactants and Products **Stay the Same**

1) Lots of changes are **reversible** — they can go **both ways**. To show a change is reversible, you stick in a $\rightleftharpoons$.

2) As the **reactants** get used up, the **forward** reaction **slows down** — and as more **product** is formed, the **reverse** reaction **speeds up**. After a while, the forward reaction will be going at exactly the **same rate** as the backward reaction.

   The amounts of reactants and products **won't be changing** any more, so it'll seem like **nothing's happening**. It's a bit like you're **digging a hole** while someone else is **filling it in** at exactly the **same speed**. This is called a **dynamic equilibrium**.

3) Equilibria can be set up in **physical** systems, e.g.:

   > When **liquid bromine** is shaken in a closed flask, some of it changes to orange **bromine gas**. After a while, **equilibrium** is reached — bromine liquid is **still** changing to bromine gas and bromine gas is still changing to bromine liquid, but they are changing at the **same rate**.
   >
   > $Br_{2(l)} \rightleftharpoons Br_{2(g)}$

   ...and **chemical** systems, e.g.:

   > If **hydrogen gas** and **iodine gas** are mixed together in a closed flask, **hydrogen iodide** is formed.
   >
   > $$H_{2(g)} + I_{2(g)} \rightleftharpoons 2HI_{(g)}$$
   >
   > Imagine that **1.0 mole** of hydrogen gas is mixed with **1.0 mole** of iodine gas at a constant temperature of **640 K**. When this mixture reaches equilibrium, there will be **1.6 moles** of hydrogen iodide and **0.2 moles** of both hydrogen gas and iodine gas. No matter how long you leave them at this temperature, the **equilibrium** amounts **never change**. As with the physical system, it's all a matter of the forward and backward rates **being equal**.

4) A **dynamic equilibrium** can only happen in a **closed system** at a **constant temperature**. *A closed system just means nothing can get in or out.*

K_c is the Equilibrium Constant

If you know the **molar concentration** of each substance at equilibrium, you can work out the **equilibrium constant**, K_c. Your value of K_c will only be true for that particular **temperature**.

Before you can calculate K_c, you have to write an **expression** for it. Here's how:

For the general reaction $aA + bB \rightleftharpoons dD + eE$, $K_c = \dfrac{[D]^d [E]^e}{[A]^a [B]^b}$

The products go on the top line. The square brackets, [ ], mean concentration in moldm^{-3}.

The lower-case letters a, b, d and e are the number of moles of each substance.

So for the reaction $H_{2(g)} + I_{2(g)} \rightleftharpoons 2HI_{(g)}$, $K_c = \dfrac{[HI]^2}{[H_2]^1 [I_2]^1} = \dfrac{[HI]^2}{[H_2][I_2]}$.

These little numbers look like the orders of reaction that you saw in rate equations. But they're not — they're the number of moles.

Calculate K_c by Sticking Numbers into the Expression

If you know the **equilibrium concentrations**, just bung them in your expression. Then with a bit of help from the old calculator, you can work out the **value** for K_c. The **units** are a bit trickier though — they **vary**, so you have to work them out after each calculation.

> **Example:** If the volume of the closed flask in the hydrogen iodide example above is 2.0 dm^3, what is the equilibrium constant for the reaction at 640 K? The equilibrium concentrations are:
> $[HI] = 0.8$ moldm^{-3}, $[H_2] = 0.1$ moldm^{-3}, and $[I_2] = 0.1$ moldm^{-3}.
>
> Just stick the concentrations into the **expression** for K_c: $K_c = \dfrac{[HI]^2}{[H_2][I_2]} = \dfrac{0.8^2}{0.1 \times 0.1} = 64$ ◄ *This is the value of K_c.*
>
> To work out the **units** of K_c put the units in the expression instead of the numbers:
>
> $K_c = \dfrac{(\text{moldm}^{-3})^2}{(\text{moldm}^{-3})(\text{moldm}^{-3})}$ — the concentration units cancel, so there are **no units** for K_c.
>
> So K_c is just **64**.

The Equilibrium Constant

You Might Need to **Work Out** the Equilibrium Concentrations

You might have to figure out some of the **equilibrium concentrations** before you can find K_c:

Example: 0.20 moles of phosphorus(V) chloride decomposes at 600 K in a vessel of 5.00 dm³. The equilibrium mixture is found to contain 0.08 moles of chlorine. Write the expression for K_c and calculate its value, including units.
$$PCl_{5(g)} \rightleftharpoons PCl_{3(g)} + Cl_{2(g)}$$

First find out how many moles of PCl_5 and PCl_3 there are at equilibrium:

The **equation** tells you that when **1 mole of PCl_5** decomposes, **1 mole of PCl_3** and **1 mole of Cl_2** are formed. So if 0.08 moles of chlorine are produced at equilibrium, then there will be **0.08 moles** of PCl_3 as well. 0.08 mol of PCl_5 must have decomposed, so there will be **0.12 moles** left (0.2 – 0.08).

Divide each number of moles by the volume of the flask to give the molar concentrations:

$[PCl_3] = [Cl_2] = 0.08 \div 5.00 = $ **0.016 moldm⁻³** $[PCl_5] = 0.12 \div 5.00 = $ **0.024 moldm⁻³**

Put the concentrations in the expression for K_c and calculate it: $K_C = \dfrac{[PCl_3][Cl_2]}{[PCl_5]} = \dfrac{[0.016][0.016]}{[0.024]} = $ **0.011**

Now find the units of K_c: $K_c = \dfrac{(moldm^{-3})(moldm^{-3})}{moldm^{-3}} = $ **moldm⁻³**   So K_c = **0.011 moldm⁻³**

K_c can be used to Find **Concentrations** in an **Equilibrium Mixture**

Example: When ethanoic acid was allowed to reach equilibrium with ethanol at 25 °C, it was found that the equilibrium mixture contained 2.0 moldm⁻³ ethanoic acid and 3.5 moldm⁻³ ethanol. The K_c of the equilibrium is 4.0 at 25 °C. What are the concentrations of the other components?
$$CH_3COOH_{(l)} + C_2H_5OH_{(l)} \rightleftharpoons CH_3COOC_2H_{5(l)} + H_2O_{(l)}$$

Put all the values you know in the K_c expression: $K_c = \dfrac{[CH_3COOC_2H_5][H_2O]}{[CH_3COOH][C_2H_5OH]} \Rightarrow 4.0 = \dfrac{[CH_3COOC_2H_5][H_2O]}{2.0 \times 3.5}$

Rearranging this gives: $[CH_3COOC_2H_5][H_2O] = 4.0 \times 2.0 \times 3.5 = 28.0$

From the equation, you know that $[CH_3COOC_2H_5] = [H_2O]$, so: $[CH_3COOC_2H_5] = [H_2O] = \sqrt{28} = 5.3$ moldm⁻³

The concentration of $CH_3COOC_2H_5$ and H_2O is 5.3 moldm⁻³

If **Conditions Change** the Position of Equilibrium Will Move

If you **change** the **concentration**, **pressure** or **temperature** of a reversible reaction, you're going to **alter** the **position of equilibrium**. This just means you'll end up with **different amounts** of reactants and products at equilibrium.

If the position of equilibrium moves to the **left**, you'll get more **reactants**. $\mathbf{H_{2(g)} + I_{2(g)}} \rightleftharpoons 2HI_{(g)}$

If the position of equilibrium moves to the **right**, you'll get more **products**. $H_{2(g)} + I_{2(g)} \rightleftharpoons \mathbf{2HI_{(g)}}$

There's a rule that lets you predict how the **position of equilibrium** will change if a **condition changes**. This rule is known as **Le Chatelier's Principle**. Here it is:

If there's a change in **concentration**, **pressure** or **temperature**, the equilibrium will move to help **counteract** the change.

So, basically, if you **raise the temperature**, the position of equilibrium will shift to try to **cool things down**. And if you **raise the pressure or concentration**, the position of equilibrium will shift to try to **reduce it**.

The Equilibrium Constant

Temperature Changes Alter K_c — Concentration Changes Don't

TEMPERATURE

1) If you **increase** the temperature, you **add heat**. The equilibrium shifts in the **endothermic (positive ΔH) direction** to absorb the heat.

2) **Decreasing** the temperature **removes heat**. The equilibrium shifts in the **exothermic (negative ΔH) direction** to try to replace the heat.

3) If the forward reaction's **endothermic**, the reverse reaction will be **exothermic**, and vice versa.

4) If the change means **more product** is formed, K_c **will rise**. If it means **less product** is formed, then K_c **will decrease**.

The reaction below is exothermic in the forward direction. If you increase the temperature, the equilibrium shifts to the left to absorb the extra heat. This means that less product's formed.

Exothermic $\longrightarrow$
$$2SO_{2(g)} + O_{2(g)} \rightleftharpoons 2SO_{3(g)} \quad \Delta H = -197 \text{ kJmol}^{-1}$$
$\longleftarrow$ Endothermic

$$K_c = \frac{[SO_3]^2}{[SO_2]^2[O_2]}$$

Since there's less product formed, K_c decreases.

CONCENTRATION

The value of the **equilibrium constant**, K_c, is **fixed** at a given temperature. So if the concentration of one thing in the equilibrium mixture **changes** then the concentrations of the others must change to keep the value of K_c the same.

$$CH_3COOH_{(l)} + C_2H_5OH_{(l)} \rightleftharpoons CH_3COOC_2H_{5(l)} + H_2O_{(l)}$$

If you increase the concentration of CH_3COOH then the equilibrium will move to the right to get rid of the extra CH_3COOH — so more $CH_3COOC_2H_5$ and H_2O are produced. This keeps the equilibrium constant the same.

Catalysts have **NO EFFECT** on the **position of equilibrium or on the value of K_c**. They **can't** increase **yield** — but they **do** mean equilibrium is approached **faster**.

Practice Questions

Q1 Write an expression for the equilibrium constant, K_c, for the reaction $N_{2(g)} + 3H_{2(g)} \rightleftharpoons 2NH_{3(g)}$.

Q2 If a reversible reaction has an exothermic forward reaction, how will increasing the temperature affect the equilibrium position?

Q3 How does adding a catalyst to a reaction affect the equilibrium position and the value of K_c?

Exam Questions

1 A sample of pure hydrogen iodide is placed in a sealed flask, and heated to 443 °C.
The following equilibrium is established: $2HI_{(g)} \rightleftharpoons H_{2(g)} + I_{2(g)}$ ($K_c = 0.02$)
At equilibrium the concentration of I_2 is found to be 0.77 moldm^{-3}. Find the equilibrium concentration of HI. [4 marks]

2 Nitrogen dioxide dissociates according to the equation $2NO_{2(g)} \rightleftharpoons 2NO_{(g)} + O_{2(g)}$.
When 42.5 g of nitrogen dioxide were heated in a vessel of volume 22.8 dm³ at 500 °C, 14.1 g of oxygen were found in the equilibrium mixture.
a) Calculate (i) the number of moles of nitrogen dioxide originally. [1 mark]
(ii) the number of moles of each gas in the equilibrium mixture. [3 marks]
b) Write an expression for K_c for this reaction. Find the value of K_c at this temperature, and give its units. [5 marks]

3 This equation shows the equilibrium that is set up when ethanoic acid is added to water:
$$CH_3COOH_{(aq)} \rightleftharpoons CH_3COO^-_{(aq)} + H^+_{(aq)}$$
a) Write an expression for K_c for this reaction. [1 mark]
b) State the effect on the equilibrium constant, K_c, of increasing the concentration of $CH_3COOH_{(aq)}$. The forward reaction is endothermic. [1 mark]
c) Describe how the equilibrium position would change if the temperature was increased. Explain your answer. [2 marks]
d) State the effect on the equilibrium constant, K_c, of increasing the reaction temperature. [1 mark]

A big K_c means heaps of product...

Most organic reactions and plenty of inorganic reactions are reversible. Sometimes the backwards reaction's about as speedy as a dead snail though, so some reactions might be thought of as only going one way. It's like if you're walking forwards, continental drift could be moving you backwards at the same time, just reeeeally slowly.

Acids, Bases and pH

Remember this stuff? Well, it's all down to Brønsted and Lowry — they've got a lot to answer for.

An Acid **Releases** Protons — a Base **Accepts** Protons

Brønsted-Lowry acids are **proton donors** — they release **hydrogen ions** (H^+) when they're mixed with water. You never get H^+ ions by themselves in water though — they're always combined with H_2O to form **hydroxonium ions, H_3O^+.**

HA is just any old acid. ⟹ $$HA_{(aq)} + H_2O_{(l)} \rightarrow H_3O^+_{(aq)} + A^-_{(aq)}$$

Brønsted-Lowry bases do the opposite — they're **proton acceptors**. When they're in solution, they grab **hydrogen ions** from water molecules.

B is just a random base. ⟹ $$B_{(aq)} + H_2O_{(l)} \rightarrow BH^+_{(aq)} + OH^-_{(aq)}$$

Acids and Bases can be **Strong** or **Weak**

1) **Strong acids dissociate** (or ionise) **almost completely** in water — **nearly all** the H^+ ions will be released. **Hydrochloric acid** is a strong acid — $HCl_{(g)} + water \rightarrow H^+_{(aq)} + Cl^-_{(aq)}$.
Strong bases (like sodium hydroxide) **ionise almost completely** in water too. E.g. $NaOH_{(s)} + water \rightarrow Na^+_{(aq)} + OH^-_{(aq)}$.

2) **Weak acids** (e.g. ethanoic or citric) dissociate only very **slightly** in water — so only small numbers of H^+ ions are formed. An **equilibrium** is set up which lies well over to the **left**. E.g. $CH_3COOH_{(aq)} \rightleftharpoons CH_3COO^-_{(aq)} + H^+_{(aq)}$.
Weak bases (such as ammonia) **only slightly dissociate** in water too. E.g. $NH_{3(aq)} + H_2O_{(l)} \rightleftharpoons NH_4^+_{(aq)} + OH^-_{(aq)}$.
Just like with weak acids, the equilibrium lies well over to the **left**.

These are really all reversible reactions, but the equilibrium lies extremely far to the right.

Protons are **Transferred** when **Acids** and **Bases** React

Acids can't just throw away their protons — they can only get rid of them if there's a **base** to accept them. In this reaction the **acid**, HA, **transfers** a proton to the **base**, B: $$HA_{(aq)} + B_{(aq)} \rightleftharpoons BH^+_{(aq)} + A^-_{(aq)}$$

It's an **equilibrium**, so if you add more **HA** or **B**, the position of equilibrium moves to the **right**. But if you add more **BH+** or **A-**, the equilibrium will move to the **left**. See page 9 for the rule about this.

When an acid is added to **water**, water acts as the **base** and accepts the proton:

$$HA_{(aq)} + H_2O_{(l)} \rightleftharpoons H_3O^+_{(aq)} + A^-_{(aq)}$$ ⟸ *The equilibrium's far to the left for weak acids, and far to the right for strong acids.*

Water Dissociates **Slightly**

Water dissociates into **hydroxonium ions** and **hydroxide ions**.

So this equilibrium exists in water:

$$H_2O_{(l)} + H_2O_{(l)} \rightleftharpoons H_3O^+_{(aq)} + OH^-_{(aq)}$$ or more simply $$H_2O_{(l)} \rightleftharpoons H^+_{(aq)} + OH^-_{(aq)}$$

And, just like for any other equilibrium reaction, you can apply the equilibrium law and write an expression for the **equilibrium constant**: $$K_c = \frac{[H^+][OH^-]}{[H_2O]}$$

Water only dissociates a **tiny amount**, so the equilibrium lies well over to the **left**. There's so much water compared to the amounts of H^+ and OH^- ions that the concentration of water is considered to have a **constant** value.

So if you multiply the expression you wrote for K_c (which is a constant) by $[H_2O]$ (another constant), you get a **constant**. This new constant is called the **ionic product of water** and it is given the symbol K_w.

$$K_w = K_c \times [H_2O] = [H^+][OH^-] \Rightarrow \boxed{K_w = [H^+][OH^-]}$$ *The units of K_w are always mol^2dm^{-6}.*

K_w always has the **same value** for an aqueous solution at a **given temperature**.

For example, at 298 K (25 °C), K_w has a value of 1.00×10^{-14} mol^2dm^{-6}.

In **pure water**, there is always **one** H^+ ion for **each** OH^- ion. So $[H^+] = [OH^-]$. That means if you are dealing with **pure water**, then you can say that $K_w = [H^+]^2$.

Acids, Bases and pH

The pH Scale is a Measure of the Hydrogen Ion Concentration

The **concentration of hydrogen ions** in a solution can vary enormously, so those wise chemists of old decided to express the concentration on a **logarithmic scale**.

$$pH = -\log_{10}[H^+]$$

$[H^+]$ is the concentration of hydrogen ions in a solution, measured in $moldm^{-3}$.

The pH scale normally goes from **0** (very acidic) to **14** (very alkaline). **pH 7** is regarded as being **neutral**.

You Can Calculate pH From Hydrogen Ion Concentration...

If you know the **hydrogen ion concentration** of a solution, you can calculate its **pH** by sticking the numbers into the **formula**.

A solution of hydrochloric acid has a hydrogen ion concentration of 0.01 $moldm^{-3}$. What is the pH of the solution?

$$pH = -\log_{10}[H^+] = -\log_{10}[0.01] = 2$$

Use the 'log' button on your calculator for this.

...Or Hydrogen Ion Concentration From pH

If you've got the **pH** of a solution, and you want to know its **hydrogen ion concentration**, then you need the **inverse** of the pH formula:

$$[H^+] = 10^{-pH}$$

Now you can use this formula to find $[H^+]$.

A solution of sulfuric acid has a pH of 1.52.
What is the hydrogen ion concentration of this solution?

$$[H^+] = 10^{-pH} = 10^{-1.52} = 0.03 \text{ moldm}^{-3} = 3 \times 10^{-2} \text{ moldm}^{-3}$$

For Strong Monoprotic Acids Hydrogen Ion Concentration = Acid Concentration

Hydrochloric acid and nitric acid (HNO_3) are **strong acids** so they ionise fully. They're also **monoprotic**, so each mole of acid produces **one mole of hydrogen ions**. This means the H^+ concentration is the **same** as the acid concentration.

Monoprotic means that each molecule of an acid will release 1 proton when it dissociates.

So for 0.1 $moldm^{-3}$ hydrochloric acid, $[H^+]$ is **0.1 $moldm^{-3}$**. Its pH = $-\log_{10}[H^+] = -\log_{10} 0.1 = $ **1.0**.
Here are a couple of examples for you:

1) Calculate the pH of 0.05 $moldm^{-3}$ nitric acid. $[H^+] = 0.05 \Rightarrow pH = -\log_{10} 0.05 = $ **1.30**

2) If a solution of hydrochloric acid has a pH of 2.45, what is the hydrogen ion concentration of the acid? $[H^+] = 10^{-2.45} = $ **3.55 × 10^{-3} moldm^{-3}**

For Strong Diprotic Acids Hydrogen Ion Concentration = Twice Acid Concentration

Each molecule of a **strong diprotic acid** releases **2 protons** when it dissociates.
Sulfuric acid is an example of a **strong diprotic acid**: $H_2SO_{4(l)} + water \rightarrow 2H^+_{(aq)} + SO_4^{2-}_{(aq)}$

There's more about diprotic acids on page 18.

So, **diprotic acids** produce **two moles of hydrogen ions** for **each mole of acid**, meaning that the H^+ concentration is twice the concentration of the acid.

So for 0.1 $moldm^{-3}$ sulfuric acid, $[H^+]$ is **0.2 $moldm^{-3}$**. Its pH will be: pH = $-\log_{10}[H^+] = -\log_{10} 0.2 = $ **0.70.**
Here's an example:

3) Calculate the pH of 0.25 $moldm^{-3}$ sulfuric acid. $[H^+] = 2 \times 0.25 = 0.5 \Rightarrow pH = -\log_{10} 0.5 = $ **0.30**

Acids, Bases and pH

Use K_w to Find the pH of a Base

Sodium hydroxide (NaOH) and potassium hydroxide (KOH) are **strong bases** that **fully ionise** in water — they donate **one mole of OH⁻ ions** per mole of base.

This means that the concentration of OH⁻ ions is the **same** as the **concentration of the base**. So for 0.02 moldm⁻³ sodium hydroxide solution, [OH⁻] is also **0.02 moldm⁻³**.

But to work out the **pH** you need to know [H⁺] — luckily this is linked to [OH⁻] through the **ionic product of water**, K_w:

$$K_w = [H^+][OH^-]$$

So if you know [OH⁻] for a **strong aqueous base** and K_w at a certain temperature, you can work out [H⁺] and then the **pH**.

> The value of K_w at 298 K is 1.0×10^{-14} mol²dm⁻⁶. Find the pH of 0.1 moldm⁻³ NaOH at 298 K.
>
> $$[OH^-] = 0.1 \text{ moldm}^{-3} \Rightarrow [H^+] = \frac{K_w}{[OH^-]} = \frac{1.0 \times 10^{-14}}{0.1} = 1.0 \times 10^{-13} \text{ moldm}^{-3}$$
>
> So pH = $-\log_{10} 1.0 \times 10^{-13}$ = **13.0**

Practice Questions

Q1 Which substance is acting as a Brønsted-Lowry base in the following equation? $HX + H_2O \rightarrow H_3O^+ + X^-$

Q2 Explain what is meant by the term 'strong acid' and give an example of one.

Q3 Define K_w and give its value at 298 K.

Q4 Define pH.

Exam Questions

1 a) How did Brønsted and Lowry define: (i) an acid,   (ii) a base.   [2 marks]
   b) Show, by writing appropriate equations, how HSO_4^- can behave as:
       (i) a Brønsted-Lowry acid,   (ii) a Brønsted-Lowry base.   [2 marks]

2 Hydrocyanic acid (HCN) is a weak acid. Define the term 'weak acid' and write a balanced equation for the equilibrium that occurs when HCN dissolves in water.   [4 marks]

3 Nitric acid, HNO_3, is a strong monoprotic acid.
   a) Explain what is meant by a monoprotic acid.   [1 mark]
   b) Find the concentration of a solution of nitric acid that has a pH value of 0.55.
       Give your answer to 2 decimal places.   [2 marks]

4 At 298 K, the value of K_w is 1.00×10^{-14} mol²dm⁻⁶.
   Find the pH of a 0.125 moldm⁻³ solution of sodium hydroxide at this temperature.
   Give your answer to 1 decimal place.   [3 marks]

5 A flask of water is heated to 30 °C. At 30 °C, the value of K_w is 1.47×10^{-14} mol²dm⁻⁶.
   a) Calculate the hydrogen ion concentration of the water in the flask.   [2 marks]
   b) Calculate the pH of the water at this temperature.   [1 mark]
   Give your answers to 2 decimal places.

Acids and bases — the Julie Andrews and Marilyn Manson of the chemistry world...

Don't confuse strong acids with concentrated acids, or weak acids with dilute acids. Strong and weak are to do with how much an acid ionises, whereas concentrated and dilute are to do with the number of moles of acid you've got per dm³. You can have a strong dilute acid, or a weak concentrated acid. And it works just the same way with bases too.

More pH Calculations

Those calculators should be nicely warmed up by now. You'll be needing that log function key again too.

To Find the pH of a Weak Acid you Use K_a (the Acid Dissociation Constant)

Weak acids **don't** ionise fully in solution, so the $[H^+]$ **isn't** the same as the acid concentration. This makes it a **bit trickier** to find their pH. You have to use yet another **equilibrium constant**, K_a:

For a weak aqueous acid, HA, you get the following equilibrium: $HA_{(aq)} \rightleftharpoons H^+_{(aq)} + A^-_{(aq)}$

As only a **tiny amount** of HA dissociates, you can assume that $[HA]_{start} = [HA]_{equilibrium}$.

So if you apply the equilibrium law, you get: $K_a = \dfrac{[H^+][A^-]}{[HA]}$

You can also assume that **all** the H^+ ions come from the **acid**, so $[H^+] = [A^-]$.

So $K_a = \dfrac{[H^+]^2}{[HA]}$ ← The units of K_a are $moldm^{-3}$.

Here's an example of how to use K_a to find the **pH** of a weak acid:

1) Find the pH of a 0.02 $moldm^{-3}$ solution of propanoic acid (CH_3CH_2COOH) at 298K. K_a for propanoic acid at this temperature is 1.30×10^{-5} $moldm^{-3}$.

First write an expression for K_a for the weak acid, then rearrange it to find $[H^+]^2$:

$K_a = \dfrac{[H^+]^2}{[CH_3CH_2COOH]} \Rightarrow [H^+]^2 = K_a[CH_3CH_2COOH] = (1.30 \times 10^{-5}) \times 0.02 = 2.60 \times 10^{-7}$

Take the square root of this number to find $[H^+]$: $[H^+] = \sqrt{2.60 \times 10^{-7}} = 5.10 \times 10^{-4}$ $moldm^{-3}$

Now use $[H^+]$ to find the pH of the acid: $pH = -\log_{10}[H^+] = -\log_{10} 5.10 \times 10^{-4} = \textbf{3.29}$

You Might Have to Find the Concentration or K_a of a Weak Acid

You don't need to know anything new for this type of calculation. You usually just have to find $[H^+]$ from the pH, then fiddle around with the K_a **expression** to find the missing bit of information.

2) The pH of an ethanoic acid (CH_3COOH) solution is 3.02 at 298 K. Calculate the molar concentration of this solution. The K_a of ethanoic acid is 1.75×10^{-5} $moldm^{-3}$ at 298 K.

Use the pH of the acid to find $[H^+]$: $[H^+] = 10^{-pH} = 10^{-3.02} = 9.55 \times 10^{-4}$ $moldm^{-3}$

Now write an expression for K_a, and rearrange it to equal $[CH_3COOH]$:

$K_a = \dfrac{[H^+]^2}{[CH_3COOH]} \Rightarrow [CH_3COOH] = \dfrac{[H^+]^2}{K_a} = \dfrac{(9.55 \times 10^{-4})^2}{1.75 \times 10^{-5}} = \textbf{0.0521 }\boldsymbol{moldm^{-3}}$

3) A solution of 0.162 $moldm^{-3}$ HCN has a pH of 5.05 at 298 K. What is the value of K_a for HCN at 298 K?

Use the pH of the acid to find $[H^+]$: $[H^+] = 10^{-pH} = 10^{-5.05} = 8.91 \times 10^{-6}$ $moldm^{-3}$

Then write an expression for K_a, and substitute in the values for $[H^+]$ and $[HCN]$:

$K_a = \dfrac{[H^+]^2}{[HCN]} = \dfrac{(8.91 \times 10^{-6})^2}{0.162} = \textbf{4.90} \times \textbf{10}^{\textbf{-10}}\textbf{ }\boldsymbol{moldm^{-3}}$

More pH Calculations

$pK_a = -\log_{10} K_a$ and $K_a = 10^{-pK_a}$

pK_a is calculated from K_a in exactly the same way as pH is calculated from $[H^+]$ — and vice versa.

So if an acid has a K_a value of 1.50×10^{-7}, then $\quad pK_a = -\log_{10}(1.50 \times 10^{-7}) = 6.82$.

Notice how pK$_a$ values aren't annoyingly tiny like K$_a$ values.

And if an acid has a pK_a value of 4.32, then $\quad K_a = 10^{-4.32} = 4.79 \times 10^{-5}$.

Just to make things that bit more complicated, there might be a pK_a value in a 'find the pH' type of question. If so, you need to convert it to K_a so that you can use the K_a expression.

> 4) Calculate the pH of 0.050 moldm^{-3} methanoic acid (HCOOH).
>   Methanoic acid has a pK_a of 3.75 at 298 K.
>
> $$K_a = 10^{-pK_a} = 10^{-3.75} = 1.78 \times 10^{-4} \text{ moldm}^{-3} \quad \longleftarrow \quad \text{First you have to convert the pK}_a \text{ to K}_a.$$
>
> $$K_a = \frac{[H^+]^2}{[HCOOH]} \implies [H^+]^2 = K_a[HCOOH] = 1.78 \times 10^{-4} \times 0.050 = 8.9 \times 10^{-6}$$
>
> $$\implies [H^+] = \sqrt{8.9 \times 10^{-6}} = 2.98 \times 10^{-3} \text{ moldm}^{-3} \qquad pH = -\log 2.98 \times 10^{-3} = \mathbf{2.53}$$

Sometimes you have to give your answer as a pK_a value. In this case, you just work out the K_a value as usual and then convert it to pK_a — and Bob's your pet hamster.

Practice Questions

Q1 Explain what is meant by the term 'weak acid' and give an example of one.

Q2 Write an equation for the reversible dissociation of the weak acid HA.

Q3 Explain how to find the pH of a weak acid.

Q4 Define pK_a.

Exam Questions

1 The value of K_a for the weak acid HA, at 298 K, is 5.60×10^{-4} moldm^{-3}.
   a) Write an expression for K_a for the weak acid HA. [1 mark]
   b) Calculate the pH of a 0.280 moldm^{-3} solution of HA at 298 K. [3 marks]

2 The pH of a 0.150 moldm^{-3} solution of a weak monoprotic acid, HX, is 2.65 at 298 K.
   a) Calculate the value of K_a for the acid HX at 298 K. [4 marks]
   b) Calculate pK_a for this acid. [1 mark]

3 Hydrocyanic acid is a weak monoprotic acid with the formula HCN.
   At 298 K it has a K_a of 4.9×10^{-10} moldm^{-3}.
   a) Write an expression for K_a for hydrocyanic acid. [1 mark]
   b) At 298 K, a solution of hydrocyanic acid has a pH of 4.15.
      Find the concentration of the solution in moldm^{-3}. [3 marks]
   c) Find the pK_a of hydrocyanic acid at 298 K. [1 mark]

4 At 298 K, the weak monoprotic acid HF has a pK_a of 3.16.
   Find the pH of a 0.5 moldm^{-3} solution of HF at 298 K. [5 marks]

My mate had a red Ka — but she drove it into a lamppost...

Strong acids have high K$_a$ values and weak acids have low K$_a$ values. For pK$_a$ values, it's the other way round — the stronger the acid, the lower the pK$_a$. If something's got p in front of it, like pH, pK$_w$ or pK$_a$, it tends to mean $-\log_{10}$ of whatever. Not all calculators work the same way, so make sure you know how to work logs out on your calculator.

pH Curves, Titrations and Indicators

If you add alkali to an acid, the pH changes in a squiggly sort of way.

Use Titration to Find the Concentration of an Acid or Alkali

Titrations allow you to find out **exactly** how much alkali is needed to **neutralise** a quantity of acid.

1) You measure out some **acid** of known concentration using a pipette and put it in a flask, along with some **appropriate indicator**.

2) First do a rough titration — add the **alkali** to the acid using a **burette** fairly quickly to get an approximate idea where the solution changes colour (the **end point**). Give the flask a regular **swirl**.

3) Now do an **accurate** titration. Run the alkali in to within 2 cm³ of the end point, then add it **drop by drop**. If you don't notice exactly when the solution changes colour you've **overshot** and your result won't be accurate.

4) **Record** the amount of alkali needed to **neutralise** the acid. It's best to **repeat** this process a few times, making sure you get very similar answers each time (within about 0.1 cm³ of each other).

You can also find out how much **acid** is needed to neutralise a quantity of **alkali**. It's exactly the same process as above, but you add **acid to alkali** instead.

Pipette
Pipettes measure only one volume of solution. Fill the pipette to just above the line, then drop the level down carefully to the line.

Burette
Burettes measure different volumes and let you add the solution drop by drop.

alkali

scale

acid and indicator

pH Curves Plot pH Against Volume of Acid or Base Added

The graphs below show the pH curves for the **different combinations** of **strong and weak** monoprotic acids and bases.

strong acid/strong base

The pH starts around **1**, as there's an excess of **strong acid**.

It finishes up around pH **13**, when you have an excess of **strong base**.

strong acid/weak base

The pH starts around **1**, as there's an excess of **strong acid**.

It finishes up around pH **9**, when you have an excess of **weak base**.

weak acid/strong base

The pH starts around **5**, as there's an excess of **weak acid**.

It finishes up around pH **13**, when you have an excess of **strong base**.

weak acid/weak base

The pH starts around **5**, as there's an excess of **weak acid**.

It finishes up around pH **9**, when you have an excess of **weak base**.

All the graphs apart from the weak acid/weak base graph have a bit that's almost vertical — this is the **equivalence point** or **end point**. At this point, a tiny amount of base causes a sudden, big change in pH — it's here that all the acid is just **neutralised**.

You don't get such a sharp change in a **weak acid/weak base** titration. If you used an indicator for this type of titration, its colour would change very **gradually**, and it would be very tricky to see the exact end point. So you're usually better off using a **pH meter** for this type of titration.

If you titrate a **base** with an **acid** instead, the **shapes** of the curves **stay the same**, but they **flip** over:

strong base/strong acid

strong base/weak acid

weak base/strong acid

weak base/weak acid

pH Curves, Titrations and Indicators

pH Curves can Help you Decide which Indicator to Use

When you use an **indicator**, you need it to change colour exactly at the **end point** of your titration. So you need to pick one that changes colour over a **narrow pH range** that lies **entirely** on the **vertical part** of the **pH curve**.

So for this titration you'd want an indicator that changed colour somewhere between pH 7 and pH 11.

Methyl orange and **phenolphthalein** are **indicators** that are often used for acid-base titrations. They each change colour over a **different pH range**:

Name of indicator	Colour at low pH	Approx. pH of colour change	Colour at high pH
Methyl orange	red	3.1 – 4.4	yellow
Phenolphthalein	colourless	8.3 – 10	pink

For a **strong acid/strong alkali** titration, you can use **either** of these indicators — there's a rapid pH change over the range for **both** indicators.

For a **strong acid/weak alkali** only **methyl orange** will do. The pH changes rapidly across the range for methyl orange, but not for phenolphthalein.

For a **weak acid/strong alkali**, **phenolphthalein** is the stuff to use. The pH changes rapidly over phenolphthalein's range, but not over methyl orange's.

For **weak acid/weak alkali** titrations there's no sharp pH change, so **no** indicator will work.

Practice Questions

Q1 Explain what 'equivalence point' means.

Q2 Why are indicators not used for weak acid/weak alkali titrations?

Q3 What indicator could you use for a weak acid/strong alkali titration?

Q4 Sketch the pH curve for a strong acid/weak alkali titration.

Exam Questions

1   A known volume of acid is titrated with a known volume of alkali.
    The pH of the solution is followed throughout the titration using a pH meter.

    a)   Suggest an acid and an alkali that may have been used in
         this titration.   [2 marks]

    b)   Suggest a suitable indicator for use in this titration.   [1 mark]

2   a)   Sketch a graph to show the shape of the pH curve for the titration of a weak acid with a weak base.
         Assume that both solutions have a concentration of 0.1 moldm^{-3}.   [2 marks]

    b)   What will the pH of the solution be at the equivalence point?   [1 mark]

3   Look at the three pH curves below labelled X, Y and Z.

X

Y

Z

    a)   Which of these curves represents the titration of sodium hydroxide with ethanoic acid?   [1 mark]

    b)   Write an equation for the reaction between sodium hydroxide and ethanoic acid.   [2 marks]

    c)   Suggest an indicator that you could use for this titration, and explain your choice.   [2 marks]

Try learning this stuff drop by drop...

Titrations involve playing with big bits of glassware that you're told not to break as they're really expensive — so you instantly become really clumsy. If you manage not to smash the burette, you'll find it easier to get accurate results if you use a dilute acid or alkali — drops of dilute acid and alkali contain fewer particles so you're less likely to overshoot.

Titration Calculations

Now you know how to do a titration, here's what you can do with the results...

You Can Use **Titration Results** to Calculate **Concentrations**

When you've done a titration you can use your results to calculate the **concentration** of your acid or base.

There are a few things you can do to make sure your titration **results** are as **accurate** as possible:

1) Measure the neutralisation volume as precisely as you possibly can. This will usually be to the **nearest 0.05 cm³**.
2) It's a good idea to **repeat** the titration at least three times and take a **mean average** titre value.
   That'll help you to make sure your answer is **reliable**.
3) Don't use any **anomalous** (unusual) results — as a rough guide, all your results should be within 0.2 cm³ of each other.

If you use a **pH meter** rather than an indicator, you can draw a pH curve of the titration and use it to work out how much acid or base is needed for neutralisation.

You do this by finding the **equivalence point** (the mid-point of the line of rapid pH change) and drawing a **vertical line downwards** until it meets the x-axis. The value at this point on the x-axis is the volume of acid or base needed.

Here's an Example **Calculation...**

Here's an example of how you can use the neutralisation volume to calculate the concentration of the acid or base:

Example: 25 cm³ of 0.5 moldm⁻³ HCl was needed to neutralise 35 cm³ of NaOH solution.
Calculate the concentration of the sodium hydroxide solution.

First write a **balanced equation** and decide **what you know** and what you **need to know**:

$$HCl + NaOH \rightarrow NaCl + H_2O$$
$$\text{25 cm}^3 \qquad \text{35 cm}^3$$
$$\text{0.5 moldm}^{-3} \qquad \text{?}$$

Now work out how many **moles of HCl** you have:

$$\text{Number of moles of HCl} = \frac{\text{concentration} \times \text{volume (cm}^3)}{1000} = \frac{0.5 \times 25}{1000} = 0.0125 \text{ moles}$$

You should remember this formula from AS — you divide by 1000 to get the volume from cm³ to dm³.

From the equation, you know 1 mole of HCl neutralises 1 mole of NaOH.

So 0.0125 moles of HCl must neutralise **0.0125** moles of NaOH.

Now it's a doddle to work out the **concentration of NaOH**.

This is just the formula above, rearranged.

$$\text{Concentration of NaOH}_{(aq)} = \frac{\text{moles of NaOH} \times 1000}{\text{volume (cm}^3)} = \frac{0.0125 \times 1000}{35} = \textbf{0.36 moldm}^{-3}$$

A **Diprotic Acid** Releases **Two Protons** When it Dissociates

A **diprotic acid** is one that can release **two protons** when it's in solution. Ethanedioic acid (HOOC-COOH) is diprotic. When ethanedioic acid reacts with a **base** like sodium hydroxide, it's **neutralised**. But the reaction happens in **two stages**, because the **two protons** are removed from the acid **separately**.

This means that when you titrate **ethanedioic acid** with a **strong base** you get a pH curve with two **equivalence points**:

The second equivalence point is at pH 8.4.
It corresponds to the loss of the second proton to the base, OH⁻.
$$HOOC-COO^-_{(aq)} + OH^-_{(aq)} \rightarrow {}^-OOC-COO^-_{(aq)} + H_2O_{(l)}$$

The first equivalence point is at pH 2.7.
It corresponds to the loss of the first proton to the base, OH⁻.
$$HOOC-COOH_{(aq)} + OH^-_{(aq)} \rightarrow HOOC-COO^-_{(aq)} + H_2O_{(l)}$$

Titration Calculations

You Can Find the **Concentration** of a **Diprotic Acid** From Titration Results Too

You can calculate the concentration of a **diprotic** acid from titration data in the same way as you did for a monoprotic acid.

Example: 25 cm^3 of ethanedioic acid, $C_2H_2O_4$, was completely neutralised by 20 cm^3 of 0.1 moldm^{-3} NaOH solution. Calculate the concentration of the ethanedioic acid solution.

Write a **balanced equation** and decide what you know and what you **need to know**:

$$C_2H_2O_4 + 2NaOH \rightarrow Na_2C_2O_4 + 2H_2O$$

25 cm^3 20 cm^3
?   0.1 moldm^{-3}

Because it's a diprotic acid, you need twice as many moles of base as moles of acid.

Now work out how many **moles of NaOH** you have:

$$\text{Number of moles of NaOH} = \frac{\text{concentration} \times \text{volume (cm}^3)}{1000} = \frac{0.1 \times 20}{1000} = 0.002 \text{ moles}$$

You know from the equation that you need 2 moles of NaOH to neutralise 1 mole of $C_2H_2O_4$.

So 0.002 moles of NaOH must neutralise (0.002 ÷ 2) = **0.001 moles of $C_2H_2O_4$**.

Now find the **concentration of $C_2H_2O_4$**.

$$\text{Concentration of } C_2H_2O_4 = \frac{\text{moles of } C_2H_2O_4 \times 1000}{\text{volume (cm}^3)} = \frac{0.001 \times 1000}{25} = \textbf{0.04 moldm}^{-3}$$

Practice Questions

Q1 Write a balanced equation for the reaction between the strong monoprotic acid HNO_3 and NaOH.

Q2 How many moles of NaOH would you need to neutralise one mole of a monoprotic acid?

Q3 What is a diprotic acid?

Q4 How many moles of NaOH would you need to neutralise one mole of a diprotic acid?

Exam Questions

1 A student performed a titration with 25 cm^3 of hydrochloric acid, adding 0.1 moldm^{-3} sodium hydroxide from a burette. The student's results are shown in the table below.

	Titration 1	Titration 2	Titration 3
Titre Volume (cm^3 of NaOH)	25.6	25.65	25.55

a) Write a balanced equation for the reaction. [1 mark]
b) (i) Calculate the average titre of sodium hydroxide that was needed to neutralise the hydrochloric acid. [1 mark]
  (ii) Use this to find the number of moles of sodium hydroxide that were needed to neutralise the acid. [2 marks]
c) Find the concentration of the hydrochloric acid. [2 marks]

2 Sulfuric acid is a diprotic acid. 25 cm^3 of this acid is needed to neutralise 35.65 cm^3 of 0.1 moldm^{-3} sodium hydroxide.
a) Write a balanced equation for the reaction. [1 mark]
b) Calculate:
  (i) The number of moles of sodium hydroxide present in the 35.65 cm^3 sample. [2 marks]
  (ii) The number of moles of sulfuric acid needed to neutralise the sodium hydroxide. [1 mark]
  (iii) The concentration of the sulfuric acid used. [2 marks]

3 What volume of 0.1 moldm^{-3} hydrochloric acid would be needed to neutralise 10 cm^3 of 0.25 moldm^{-3} sodium hydroxide? [6 marks]

Diprotic acids — twice the titration fun...

And that's a whole lot of calculation-based merriment. Don't forget, if it's a diprotic acid that you're using, you need twice as many moles of NaOH to neutralise it as you would a monoprotic acid. But when it comes down to it, it's the same story as any other chemistry calculation — write out the equation, compare the number of moles, and put the values into the right formula.

Buffer Action

How can a solution resist becoming more acidic if you add acid to it? Why would it want to? Here's where you find out...

Buffers Resist Changes in pH

A **buffer** is a solution that **resists** changes in pH when **small** amounts of acid or alkali are added.

A buffer **doesn't** stop the pH from changing completely — it does make the changes **very slight** though.
Buffers only work for small amounts of acid or alkali — put too much in and they'll go "Waah" and not be able to cope.
You get **acidic buffers** and **basic buffers**.

Acidic Buffers are Made from a Weak Acid and one of its Salts

Acidic buffers have a pH of less than 7 — they're made by mixing a **weak acid** with one of its **salts**.
Ethanoic acid and **sodium ethanoate** ($CH_3COO^-Na^+$) is a good example:

The ethanoic acid is a **weak acid**, so it only **slightly** dissociates: $CH_3COOH_{(aq)} \rightleftharpoons H^+_{(aq)} + CH_3COO^-_{(aq)}$.

But the salt **fully** dissociates into its ions when it dissolves: $CH_3COONa_{(s)} + water \rightarrow CH_3COO^-_{(aq)} + Na^+_{(aq)}$.

So in the solution you've got heaps of **undissociated ethanoic acid molecules**, and heaps of **ethanoate ions** from the salt.

When you alter the **concentration** of H^+ or OH^- ions in the buffer solution the **equilibrium position** moves
to **counteract** the change (this is down to **Le Chatelier's principle** — see page 9). Here's how it all works:

Lots of undissociated weak acid

Addition of H⁺ (acid)

$$CH_3COOH_{(aq)} \rightleftharpoons H^+_{(aq)} + CH_3COO^-_{(aq)}$$

Addition of OH⁻ (base)

Lots of CH_3COO^- from the dissociated salt

If you add a **small** amount of **acid** the **H^+ concentration** increases. Most of the extra H^+ ions
combine with CH_3COO^- ions to form CH_3COOH. This shifts the equilibrium to the **left**,
reducing the H^+ concentration to close to its original value. So the **pH** doesn't change.

The large number of CH_3COO^- ions make sure that the buffer can cope with the addition of acid.

There's no problem doing this as there's loads of spare CH_3COOH molecules.

If a **small** amount of **base** (e.g. NaOH) is added, the **OH^- concentration** increases.
Most of the extra OH^- ions react with H^+ ions to form water — removing H^+ ions from the solution.
This causes more CH_3COOH to **dissociate** to form H^+ ions — shifting the equilibrium to the **right**.
The H^+ concentration increases until it's close to its original value, so the **pH** doesn't change.

Basic Buffers are Made from a Weak Base and one of its Salts

Basic buffers have a pH greater than 7 — and they're made by mixing a **weak base** with one of its **salts**.
A solution of **ammonia** (NH_3, a weak base) and **ammonium chloride** (NH_4Cl, a salt of ammonia) acts as a **basic** buffer.
The **salt** fully dissociates in solution: $NH_4Cl_{(aq)} \rightarrow NH_4^+_{(aq)} + Cl^-_{(aq)}$.
Some of the NH_3 molecules will also react with water molecules: $NH_{3(aq)} + H_2O_{(aq)} \rightleftharpoons NH_4^+_{(aq)} + OH^-_{(aq)}$.
So the solution will contain loads of **ammonium ions** (NH_4^+), and lots of **ammonia** molecules too.

The **equilibrium position** of this reaction
can move to **counteract** changes in pH:

Addition of H⁺ (acid)

Lots of NH_4^+

Lots of weak base

$$NH_{3(aq)} + H_2O_{(l)} \rightleftharpoons NH_4^+_{(aq)} + OH^-_{(aq)}$$

Addition of OH⁻ (base)

If a small amount of **base** is added, the OH^- concentration **increases**, making the solution more **alkaline**.
Most of the extra OH^- ions will react with the NH_4^+ ions, to form NH_3 and H_2O. So the equilibrium
will shift to the **left**, removing OH^- ions from the solution, and stopping the pH from changing much.

If a small amount of **acid** is added, the H^+ concentration **increases**, making the solution more **acidic**.
- Some of the H^+ ions react with **OH^-** ions to make **H_2O**. When this happens the equilibrium position
  moves to the right to replace the OH^- ions that have been used up.
- Some of the H^+ ions react with **NH_3** molecules to form NH_4^+: $NH_3 + H^+ \rightleftharpoons NH_4^+$
These reactions will **remove** most of the extra H^+ ions that were added — so the pH **won't** change much.

Buffer Action

Here's How to Calculate the pH of a Buffer Solution

Calculating the **pH** of an acidic buffer isn't too tricky. You just need to know the K_a of the weak acid and the **concentrations** of the weak acid and its salt. Here's how to go about it:

Example: A buffer solution contains 0.40 moldm^{-3} methanoic acid, HCOOH, and 0.6 moldm^{-3} sodium methanoate, HCOO$^-$Na$^+$. For methanoic acid, $K_a = 1.6 \times 10^{-4}$ moldm^{-3}. What is the pH of this buffer?

Firstly, write the expression for K_a of the weak acid:

$$HCOOH_{(aq)} \rightleftharpoons H^+_{(aq)} + HCOO^-_{(aq)} \implies K_a = \frac{\left[H^+_{(aq)}\right] \times \left[HCOO^-_{(aq)}\right]}{\left[HCOOH_{(aq)}\right]}$$

Remember — these all have to be equilibrium concentrations.

Then rearrange the expression and stick in the data to calculate $[H^+_{(aq)}]$:

$$\left[H^+_{(aq)}\right] = K_a \times \frac{\left[HCOOH_{(aq)}\right]}{\left[HCOO^-_{(aq)}\right]}$$

$$\implies \left[H^+_{(aq)}\right] = 1.6 \times 10^{-4} \times \frac{0.4}{0.6} = 1.07 \times 10^{-4} \text{ moldm}^{-3}$$

You have to make a **few assumptions** here:
• HCOO$^-$Na$^+$ is fully dissociated, so assume that the equilibrium concentration of HCOO$^-$ is the same as the initial concentration of HCOO$^-$Na$^+$.
• HCOOH is only slightly dissociated, so assume that its equilibrium concentration is the same as its initial concentration.

Finally, convert $[H^+_{(aq)}]$ to pH: $pH = -\log_{10}[H^+_{(aq)}] = -\log_{10}(1.07 \times 10^{-4}) = \mathbf{3.97}$ And that's your answer.

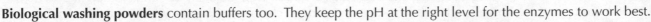

Buffers are Really Handy

Jeremy resolved to use a shampoo with a buffer in future.

Most **shampoos** contain a pH 5.5 buffer — it counteracts the alkaline soap in the shampoo. The soap might get your hair squeaky clean, but alkalis don't make your hair look shiny.

Biological washing powders contain buffers too. They keep the pH at the right level for the enzymes to work best.

There are also lots of **biological buffer** systems in our bodies, making sure all our tissues are kept at the **right pH**. For example, it's vital that **blood** stays at a pH very near to 7.4, so it contains a buffer system.

Practice Questions

Q1 What's a buffer solution?

Q2 How can a mixture of ethanoic acid and sodium ethanoate act as a buffer?

Q3 Describe how to make a basic buffer.

Q4 Give two uses of buffer solutions.

Exam Questions

1 A buffer solution contains 0.40 moldm^{-3} benzoic acid, C$_6$H$_5$COOH, and 0.20 moldm^{-3} sodium benzoate, C$_6$H$_5$COO$^-$Na$^+$. At 25 °C, K$_a$ for benzoic acid is 6.4×10^{-5} moldm^{-3}.

   a) Calculate the pH of the buffer solution. [3 marks]

   b) Explain the effect on the buffer of adding a small quantity of dilute sulfuric acid. [3 marks]

2 A buffer was prepared by mixing solutions of butanoic acid, CH$_3$(CH$_2$)$_2$COOH, and sodium butanoate, CH$_3$(CH$_2$)$_2$COO$^-$Na$^+$, so that they had the **same** concentration.

   a) Write a chemical equation to show butanoic acid acting as a weak acid. [1 mark]

   b) Given that K$_a$ for butanoic acid is 1.5×10^{-5} moldm^{-3}, calculate the pH of the buffer solution. [3 marks]

Old buffers are often resistant to change...

So that's how buffers work — add acid, and the equilibrium moves one way, add alkali and it moves the other. That way you don't end up changing the concentration of hydrogen ions in the solution, so the pH doesn't change either. There's a pleasing simplicity about it that I find rather elegant. Like a fine wine with a nose of berry and undertones of... OK, I'll shut up now.

Naming Organic Compounds

There are zillions of organic compounds. And loads of them are pretty similar — just with slight, but crucial differences. There's no way you could memorise all their names, so chemists have devised a clever way of naming each of them.

Nomenclature is a Fancy Word for Naming Organic Compounds

You can name **any** organic compound using **rules** of nomenclature.

Here's how to use the rules to name a **branched alcohol**.

1) Count the carbon atoms in the **longest continuous chain** — this gives you the stem:

Don't forget — the longest carbon chain may be bent.

Number of carbons	1	2	3	4	5	6	7	8	9	10
Stem	meth-	eth-	prop-	but-	pent-	hex-	hept-	oct-	non-	dec-

2) The **main functional group** of the molecule usually gives you the end of the name (the **suffix**).

Homologous series	Prefix or Suffix	Example
alkanes	-ane	Propane $CH_3CH_2CH_3$
branched alkanes	-yl	methylpropane $CH_3CH(CH_3)CH_3$
cycloalkanes	cyclo-	cyclohexane C_6H_{12}
alkenes	-ene	propene $CH_3CH=CH_2$
haloalkanes	chloro- bromo- iodo-	chloroethane CH_3CH_2Cl
alcohols	-ol	ethanol CH_3CH_2OH

The longest chain is **5** carbons, so the stem is **pent-**

The main functional group is **-OH**, so the compound's name is going to be based on "**pentanol**".

3) Number the carbons in the **longest** carbon chain so that the carbon with the main functional group attached has the lowest possible number. If there's more than one longest chain, pick the one with the **most side-chains**.

4) Write the carbon number that the functional group is on **before the suffix**.

5) Any side-chains or less important functional groups are added as prefixes at the start of the name. Put them in **alphabetical** order, with the **number** of the carbon atom each is attached to.

Longest chain with most side-chains

-OH has lowest possible number.

–OH is on carbon-2, so it's some sort of "**pentan-2-ol**".

6) If there's more than one **identical** side-chain or functional group, use **di-** (2), **tri-** (3) or **tetra-** (4) before that part of the name — but ignore this when working out the alphabetical order.

There's an ethyl group on carbon-3, and methyl groups on carbon-2 and carbon-4, so it's **3-ethyl-2,4-dimethylpentan-2-ol**

You Can Name Haloalkanes Using These Rules

Haloalkanes are just alkanes where one or more hydrogens have been swapped for a **halogen.** You can name them using the rules above.

dichloromethane   trichloromethane   2-iodopropane   2-bromo-2-chloro-1, 1, 1-trifluoroethane

Naming Organic Compounds

Naming *Alkenes* — *Look at the Position of the* **Double Bond**

Alkenes have at least one **double bond** in their carbon chain.
For alkenes with more than three carbons, you need to say which carbon the double bond starts from.

Example 1) The longest chain is **5** carbons, so the stem of the name is **pent-**.

2) The functional group is **C=C**, so it's **pentene**.

3) Number the carbons from right to left (so the double bond starts on the lowest possible number). The first carbon in the double bond is **carbon 2**. So this is **pent-2-ene**.

Here are some more examples:

propene CH_2CHCH_3

Pent-2-ene $CH_3CHCHCH_2CH_3$

buta-1,3-diene $CH_2CHCHCH_2$

If the alkene has two double bonds, the suffix becomes **diene**. *When there's more than one double bond, the stem of the name usually gets an extra 'a' too (e.g. but**a**- or pent**a**- not but- or pent-). And you might see the numbers written first, e.g. 1,3-butadiene.*

Alcohols can be *Primary*, *Secondary* or *Tertiary*

1) The alcohol homologous series has the **general formula $C_nH_{2n+1}OH$**.

2) An alcohol is **primary**, **secondary** or **tertiary**, depending on which carbon atom the hydroxyl group **–OH** is bonded to...

Primary (1°)   R=alkyl group   E.g. Propan–1–ol

Secondary (2°)   E.g. Propan–2–ol

Tertiary (3°)   E.g. 2–methylpropan–2–ol

Practice Questions

Q1 Name the haloalkane shown in the diagram on the right.

Q2 How many carbon atoms are there in 2-methylpropane? Draw its structure.

Q3 Write out the general formula for an alcohol, and draw an example of a tertiary alcohol.

Exam Questions

1   A diene is reacted with hydrogen bromide, HBr, to give a mixture of haloalkanes, including haloalkanes A and B:

A

B

a) Name haloalkane A. [1 mark]

b) Name haloalkane B. [1 mark]

c) Draw and name the diene molecule that both haloalkanes were formed from. [2 marks]

2   A secondary alcohol has the molecular formula $C_4H_{10}O$.
It can be dehydrated to form two different alkenes, both of which have the molecular formula C_4H_8.

a) Draw the structure of the secondary alcohol, and name it. [2 marks]

b) Give the names of the two different alkenes that can be formed by dehydrating the alcohol. [2 marks]

It's as easy as 1,2,3-trichloropent-2-ene...

The best thing to do now is find some random alkanes, alkenes, haloalkanes and alcohols, and work out their names using the rules. Then have a bash at it the other way around — read the name and draw the compound. It might seem a wee bit tedious now, but come the exam, you'll be thanking me. Doing the exam questions will give you some good practice too.

Formulas and Isomers

If you thought the last page was a bit wordy, this one's all about how a molecule's atoms are actually arranged, and how you can represent its shape on paper.

There are **Loads of Ways** of Representing Organic Compounds

TYPE OF FORMULA	WHAT IT SHOWS YOU	FORMULA FOR BUTAN-1-OL
General formula	An algebraic formula that can describe **any member** of a family of compounds.	$C_nH_{2n+1}OH$ (for all alcohols)
Empirical formula	The **simplest ratio** of atoms of each element in a compound (cancel the numbers down if possible). (So ethane, C_2H_6, has the empirical formula CH_3.)	$C_4H_{10}O$
Molecular formula	The **actual** number of atoms of each element in a molecule, with any **functional groups** indicated.	C_4H_9OH
Structural formula	Shows the atoms **carbon by carbon**, with the attached hydrogens and functional groups.	$CH_3CH_2CH_2CH_2OH$
Displayed formula	Shows how all the atoms are **arranged**, and all the bonds between them.	(displayed structure of butan-1-ol)
Skeletal formula	Shows the **bonds** of the carbon skeleton **only**, with any functional groups. The hydrogen and carbon atoms aren't shown. This is handy for drawing large complicated structures, like cyclic hydrocarbons.	(skeletal structure) OH

> A functional group is a reactive part of a molecule — it gives it most of its chemical properties.

A **homologous series** is a bunch of organic compounds which have the **same general formula**. **Alkanes** are a homologous series. Each member of a homologous series differs by **–CH₂–**.

Structural Isomers have different Structural Arrangements of Atoms

In structural isomers, the atoms are **connected** in different ways. But they still have the **same molecular formula**. There are **three types** of structural isomers:

CHAIN ISOMERS

Chain isomers have different arrangements of the **carbon skeleton**. Some are **straight chains** and others **branched** in different ways.

butane   **methylpropane**

POSITIONAL ISOMERS

Positional isomers have the **same skeleton** and the **same atoms or groups of atoms** attached. The difference is that the **functional group** is attached to a **different carbon atom**.

1-chlorobutane   **2-chlorobutane**

FUNCTIONAL GROUP ISOMERS

Functional group isomers have the same atoms arranged into **different functional groups**.

propanal   **propanone**   **cyclopropanol**

> These are all functional group isomers of C_3H_6O.

Formulas and Isomers

E/Z isomerism is a Type of Stereoisomerism

The astronauts liked to arrange things differently in space.

1) **Stereoisomers** have the same structural formula but a **different arrangement** in space. (Just bear with me for a moment... that will become clearer, I promise.)

2) You can **twist** and **rotate** a molecule any way you like around a **single bond**. But a **double bond** has a **fixed position** — you **can't** rotate the rest of the molecule around it.

3) Because of the **lack of rotation** around the double bond, some **alkenes** have stereoisomers.

4) Stereoisomers happen when each double-bonded carbon atom has two **different atoms** or **groups** attached to it. Then you get an '**E-isomer**' and a '**Z-isomer**'.

For example, the double-bonded carbon atoms in but-2-ene each have an **H** and a **CH₃** group attached.

When the same groups are **across** the double bond then it's the **E-isomer**. This molecule is **E-but-2-ene**.

E stands for 'entgegen', a German word meaning 'opposite'.

When the same groups are **both above** or **both below** the double bond then it's the Z-isomer. This molecule is **Z-but-2-ene**.

Z stands for 'zusammen', the German for 'together'.

Practice Questions

Q1 Explain what the term 'general formula' means.

Q2 Give both the empirical formula and the molecular formula of methylpropane.

Q3 Explain why 1,1-dichloropropane and 1,2-dichloropropane are positional isomers.

Q4 What are stereoisomers?

Exam Questions

1 A chemist has samples of three chemicals, labelled A, B and C.

   a) Chemical A is a straight chain alcohol with the molecular formula $C_5H_{11}OH$.
      Give the names of two positional isomers that fit this description. [2 marks]

   b) Chemical B is an alkene with the molecular formula C_5H_{10}.
      Give the names of a pair of stereoisomers with this molecular formula. [2 marks]

   c) Chemical C is a hydrocarbon with the molecular formula C_3H_6.
      Give the names of two functional group isomers with this molecular formula. [2 marks]

2 The ethers are a homologous series of hydrocarbon molecules.
   The structural formulas of three members of the series are shown below.

CH_3OCH_3	$CH_3CH_2OCH_3$	$CH_3CH_2OCH_2CH_3$
Methoxymethane	**Ethoxymethane**	**Ethoxyethane**

   a) Give the empirical formula of ethoxyethane [1 mark]

   b) Write the general formula of the ether family. [1 mark]

   c) Use your general formula to predict the empirical formula of an ether molecule with ten carbon atoms. [1 mark]

   d) Draw the displayed formula of a functional group isomer of methoxymethane. [1 mark]

Human structural isomers...

Optical Isomerism

As if E/Z isomerism wasn't exciting enough, take a deep breath and prepare for stereoisomerism part two — optical isomerism...

Optical Isomers are Mirror Images of Each Other

Optical isomerism is another type of stereoisomerism. Stereoisomers have the **same structural formula**, but have their atoms arranged differently in **space**.

A **chiral** (or **asymmetric**) carbon atom is one that has **four different groups** attached to it. It's possible to arrange the groups in two different ways around the carbon atom so that two different molecules are made — these molecules are called **enantiomers** or **optical isomers**.

The enantiomers are **mirror images** and no matter which way you turn them, they can't be **superimposed**.

> If the molecules can be superimposed, they're <u>achiral</u> — and there's no optical isomerism.

You have to be able to draw optical isomers. But first you have to identify the chiral centre...

Example

Locating the chiral centre:
Look for the carbon atom with four different groups attached. Here it's the carbon with the four groups H, OH, CHO and CH_3 attached.

chiral centre

2-hydroxypropanoic acid

Drawing isomers:
Once you know the chiral carbon, draw one enantiomer in a tetrahedral shape. Don't try to draw the full structure of each group — it gets confusing. Then draw a mirror image beside it.

enantiomers of 2-hydroxypropanoic acid

Optical Isomers Rotate Plane-Polarised Light

Optical isomers are **optically active** — they **rotate plane-polarised light**. One enantiomer rotates it in a **clockwise** direction, and the other rotates it in an **anticlockwise** direction.

> Normal light vibrates in all directions, but plane-polarised light only vibrates in one direction.

Most Optical Isomers are Produced as Racemates in the Laboratory

A **racemate** (or **racemic mixture**) contains **equal quantities** of each enantiomer of an optically active compound.

Racemates **don't** show any optical activity — the two enantiomers **cancel** each other's light-rotating effect.
Chemists often react two **achiral** things together and get a **racemic** mixture of a **chiral** product.
This is because when two molecules react there's an **equal chance** of forming each of the enantiomers.
Look at the reaction between butane and chlorine:

Butane $+ Cl_2 \longrightarrow HCl +$ **Enantiomer 1**   or   **Enantiomer 2**   **Enantiomer 1**   **Enantiomer 2**

A **chlorine atom** replaces one of the H groups, to give **2-chlorobutane**.
Either of the H groups can be replaced, so the reaction produces a **mixture of the two possible enantiomers**.
Each hydrogen has a **fifty-fifty chance** of being replaced, so the two optical isomers are formed in **equal amounts**.

You can modify a reaction to produce a **single enantiomer** using chemical methods, but it's **difficult** and **expensive**.

Optical Isomerism

Pharmaceutical Drugs Must Only Contain a Single Optical Isomer

Drugs work by changing **chemical reactions** that are taking place in the body.
Most drugs do this by binding to an **active site** — usually on an **enzyme** or a specific **receptor** molecule.

A drug must be **exactly** the right **shape** to fit into the correct active site — only one enantiomer will do.
The other enantiomer could fit into a different enzyme, and might cause **harmful side-effects** or have **no effect** at all.
So if a drug happens to be chiral, it must be made so that it only contains one enantiomer.

Thalidomide is an example of a drug whose optical isomers have different effects.

1) Thalidomide was developed in the 1950s as a **sedative** drug. **Early tests** seemed to show that it had **few side effects**, and so it was launched as a prescription drug.

2) Thalidomide also proved to be an effective **anti-sickness** drug. It was widely prescribed to **pregnant women** in the late 1950s and early 1960s to combat **morning sickness**.

3) At the same time babies began to be born with **malformed limbs** — thalidomide was shown to be causing these symptoms, and its use was **banned**.

4) The drug had **not been tested thoroughly** enough, particularly in relation to its possible **effects on the developing foetus**.

5) Further studies demonstrated that the two **optical isomers** have **different effects** in the body. One is an effective **anti-sickness** drug. The other can cause **birth defects**. In this case even if a **pure dose** of the safe isomer is given, the body will **convert** some of it to the harmful isomer.

6) More recent research has shown that thalidomide can be useful for treating **other diseases**, such as some types of cancer. Patients can now be treated with thalidomide, but **very strict controls** are in place to ensure that it is **never** taken by anyone who is pregnant.

Practice Questions

Q1 What's a chiral molecule?
Q2 What's a racemic mixture?
Q3 The displayed formula of 2-methylbutan-1-al is shown on the right. Explain why the carbon atom marked with a * is a chiral centre.
Q4 Explain why most optically active pharmaceutical drugs only contain one isomer.

Exam Questions

1 There are sixteen possible structural isomers of the compound $C_3H_6O_2$, four of which show stereoisomerism.

a) Explain the meaning of the term *stereoisomerism*. [2 marks]

b) Draw a pair of stereoisomers of $C_3H_6O_2$, with hydroxyl groups. Label them *E* and *Z*. [3 marks]

c) (i) There are two chiral isomers of $C_3H_6O_2$. Draw the enantiomers of one of the chiral isomers. [2 marks]
(ii) What structural feature in the molecule gives rise to optical isomerism? [1 mark]
(iii) State how you could distinguish between the enantiomers. [2 marks]

2 Parkinson's disease involves a deficiency of dopamine. It is treated by giving patients a single pure enantiomer of DOPA (dihydroxyphenylalanine), a naturally occurring amino acid, which is converted to dopamine in the brain.

a) DOPA is a chiral molecule. Its structure is shown on the right. Mark the structure's chiral centre. [1 mark]

b) A DOPA racemate was synthesised in 1911, but today a natural form of the pure DOPA enantiomer is isolated from fava beans for use as a pharmaceutical.
(i) Explain the meaning of the term *racemate*. [1 mark]
(ii) Suggest two reasons why the pure DOPA enantiomer is used in preference to the racemate. [2 marks]

Time for some quiet reflection...

This isomer stuff's not all bad — you get to draw little pretty pictures of molecules. If you're having difficulty picturing them as 3D shapes, you could always make some models with matchsticks and plasticine®. It's easier to see the mirror image structure with a solid version in front of you. And if you become a famous artist, you can sell them for millions...

UNIT 4: SECTION 2 — BASIC ORGANIC CHEMISTRY & ISOMERISM

Aldehydes and Ketones

Aldehydes and ketones are closely related compounds, with one wee, but crucial, difference...

Aldehydes and Ketones contain a Carbonyl Group

Aldehydes and ketones are both **carbonyl compounds** so they both contain the **carbonyl** functional group, **C=O**. The difference is, they've got their carbonyl groups in **different positions**.

Aldehydes have their carbonyl group at the **end** of the carbon chain. Their names end in **–al**.

'R' represents a carbon chain of any length.

methanal   propanal

Ketones have their carbonyl group in the middle of the carbon chain. Their names end in **–one**, and often have a number to show which **carbon** the carbonyl group is on.

propanone   pentan-2-one

There are a Few Tests to Distinguish Between Aldehydes and Ketones

They all work on the idea that an **aldehyde** can be **easily oxidised** to a carboxylic acid, but a ketone can't.

aldehyde

$$R - C + [O] \longrightarrow R - C$$

ketone

$$R - C + [O] \longrightarrow \quad \textbf{✗}$$
nothing happens

As an aldehyde is oxidised, another compound is **reduced** — so a reagent is used that **changes colour** as it's reduced.

TOLLENS' REAGENT

Tollens' reagent is a **colourless** solution of **silver nitrate** dissolved in **aqueous ammonia**.

If it's heated in a test tube with an aldehyde, a **silver mirror** forms after a few minutes.

$$\underset{\text{colourless}}{Ag(NH_3)_2^+}{}_{(aq)} + e^- \longrightarrow \underset{\text{silver}}{Ag_{(s)}} + 2NH_{3(aq)}$$

The aldehyde/ketone will be flammable, so heat the mixture in a water bath rather than over a flame.

FEHLING'S SOLUTION OR BENEDICT'S SOLUTION

Fehling's solution is a **blue** solution of complexed **copper(II) ions** dissolved in **sodium hydroxide**.

If it's heated with an aldehyde the copper(II) ions are reduced to a **brick-red precipitate** of **copper(I) oxide**.

$$\underset{\text{blue}}{Cu^{2+}}{}_{(aq)} + e^- \longrightarrow \underset{\text{brick-red}}{Cu^+}{}_{(s)}$$

Benedict's solution is exactly the same as Fehling's solution except the copper(II) ions are dissolved in **sodium carbonate** instead. You still get a **brick-red precipitate** of copper(I) oxide though.

You can Reduce Aldehydes and Ketones Back to Alcohols

In AS Chemistry you saw how **primary alcohols** can be **oxidised** to produce **aldehydes** and **carboxylic acids**, and how **secondary alcohols** can be **oxidised** to make **ketones**. Using a **reducing agent** you can **reverse** these reactions.

NaBH$_4$ (sodium tetrahydridoborate(III) or sodium borohydride) dissolved in **water with methanol** is usually the reducing agent used. But in equations, **[H]** is often used to indicate a hydrogen from a reducing agent.

1) Reducing an **aldehyde** to a **primary alcohol**.

$$R - C\underset{H}{\overset{O}{}} + 2[H] \longrightarrow R - CH_2 - OH$$

Here's the reaction mechanism:

2) Reducing a **ketone** to a **secondary alcohol**.

$$R - C\underset{R'}{\overset{O}{}} + 2[H] \longrightarrow R - \underset{R'}{\overset{H}{C}} - OH$$

The reaction mechanism for ketones is the same as for aldehydes.

The H⁻ ions (Ḧ) come from the reducing agent.

The H⁺ ions usually come from water. Sometimes a weak acid is added as a source of H⁺.

These are **nucleophilic addition** reactions. The H⁻ ion acts as a **nucleophile** and **adds** on to the δ⁺ carbon atom.

Aldehydes and Ketones

Hydrogen Cyanide will React with Carbonyls by Nucleophilic Addition

Hydrogen cyanide reacts with carbonyl compounds to produce **hydroxynitriles** (molecules with a CN and an OH group). It's a **nucleophilic addition reaction** — a **nucleophile** attacks the molecule, causing an extra group to be **added**.

Hydrogen cyanide's a **weak acid** — it partially dissociates in water to form **H^+** ions and **CN^-** ions. $HCN \rightleftharpoons H^+ + CN^-$

1) The CN^- group **attacks** the partially positive carbon atom and **donates** a pair of electrons. Both electrons from the double bond transfer to the oxygen.

2) H^+ (from either hydrogen cyanide or water) bonds to the oxygen to form the **hydroxyl group** (OH).

The carbonyl group has a dipole.

CN^- is a nucleophile.

hydroxynitrile

There's an extra carbon atom.

Do a Risk Assessment Before Combining Any Chemicals

A risk assessment involves **reviewing the hazards** of the reacting chemicals, the products and any conditions needed, such as heat. You don't have to wrap yourself in cotton wool, but you do have to take **all reasonable precautions** to reduce the risk of an accident.

Here's a bit of a risk assessment for reacting hydrogen cyanide with a carbonyl compound (above):
Hydrogen cyanide is a highly toxic gas. So to reduce the risk, a solution of acidified potassium cyanide is used instead. The cyanide ions needed for the reaction are formed in the solution. Even so, the reaction should be done in a fume cupboard. Also, the organic compounds are flammable, so if you need to heat them use a water bath or electric mantle.

Practice Questions

Q1 What's the difference between the structures of aldehydes and ketones?

Q2 Describe a chemical test that lets you distinguish between aldehydes and ketones.

Q3 Explain why the reduction of an aldehyde or a ketone is a nucleophilic addition reaction.

Q4 Why is acidified KCN preferred to HCN as a reagent in the reaction: $CH_3CHO + HCN \rightarrow CH_3CH(OH)CN$?

Exam Question

1   The compound C_3H_6O can exist as an aldehyde and a ketone.

  a) Draw and name the carbonyl isomers of C_3H_6O.   [4 marks]

  b) Hydrogen cyanide, HCN, will react with C_3H_6O carbonyl compounds to form a compound with the molecular formula C_4H_6ON.

    (i)   Name the type of mechanism that this reaction proceeds by.   [1 mark]

    (ii)   Draw the different products formed when the carbonyl compound is an aldehyde and a ketone.
         Indicate which product will be produced as a racemic mixture and explain why.   [4 marks]

  c) The aldehyde C_3H_6O can be reduced to an alcohol, C_3H_7OH.

    (i)   Write an equation for the reaction. Show the structures of the aldehyde and alcohol clearly.   [1 mark]

    (ii)   Suggest suitable reagent(s) and conditions for the reaction.   [2 marks]

2   There are two straight-chain carbonyl compounds with the molecular formula C_4H_8O.

  a) Name the two compounds.   [2 marks]

  b) Name a reagent that could be used to distinguish between the isomers and give the expected result for each.   [3 marks]

  c) During the above test one of the isomers is converted to a carboxylic acid.
    Name the organic product of the reaction.   [1 mark]

There ain't nobody nowhere gonna oxidise me...

You've got to be a dab hand at recognising functional groups from a mile off. The carbonyl group's just the first of many. Make sure you know how aldehydes differ from ketones and what you get when you oxidise or reduce them both. The mechanisms are a pain to learn, but you've just got to do it. Keep trying to write them out from memory till you can.

Carboxylic Acids and Esters

Carboxylic acids are much more interesting than cardboard boxes — as you're about to discover...

Carboxylic Acids contain –COOH

> A <u>carboxyl</u> group contains a <u>carbonyl</u> group and a hydr<u>oxyl</u> group.

Carboxylic acids contain the **carboxyl** functional group **–COOH**.

To name them, you find and name the longest alkane chain, take off the 'e' and add **'–oic acid'**.

ethanoic acid   4-hydroxy-2-methylbutanoic acid   benzoic acid

> See page 36 for more about naming benzene compounds.

The carboxyl group is always at the **end** of the molecule and when naming it's more important than other functional groups — so all the other functional groups in the molecule are numbered starting from this carbon.

Carboxylic Acids are Weak Acids

Carboxylic acids are **weak acids** — in water they partially dissociate into a **carboxylate ion** and an **H⁺ ion**.

The equilibrium lies to the left because most of the molecules don't dissociate.

carboxylic acid   carboxylate ion

Pete was hoping for an A⁻ in his carboxylic acid practical, but he ended up with an H⁺.

Carboxylic Acids React with Carbonates to Form Carbon Dioxide

Carboxylic acids react with **carbonates**, CO_3^{2-} or **hydrogencarbonates**, HCO_3^- to form a **salt**, **carbon dioxide** and **water**.

ethanoic acid   sodium ethanoate

$$2CH_3COOH_{(aq)} + Na_2CO_{3(s)} \rightarrow 2CH_3COONa_{(aq)} + H_2O_{(l)} + CO_{2(g)}$$

$$CH_3COOH_{(aq)} + NaHCO_{3(s)} \rightarrow CH_3COONa_{(aq)} + H_2O_{(l)} + CO_{2(g)}$$

> In these reactions, carbon dioxide fizzes out of the solution.

Carboxylic Acids React with Alcohols to form Esters

> There's more on esters at the top of the next page.

If you heat a **carboxylic acid** with an **alcohol** in the presence of a **strong acid catalyst**, you get an ester. It's called an **esterification** reaction. Concentrated sulfuric acid is usually used as the acid catalyst.

carboxylic acid   alcohol   ester   water

This oxygen comes from the alcohol.

> It's also a condensation reaction as it releases water.

Here's how ethanoic acid reacts with ethanol to make the ester, ethyl ethanoate:

ethanoic acid   ethanol   ethyl ethanoate   water

Carboxylic Acids and Esters

Esters have the Functional Group –COO–

You've just seen that an ester is formed by reacting an alcohol with a carboxylic acid. Well, the **name** of an **ester** is made up of **two parts** — the **first** bit comes from the **alcohol**, and the **second** bit from the **carboxylic acid**.

1) Look at the **alkyl group** that came from the **alcohol**. This is the first bit of the ester's name.

This is an **ethyl** group.

2) Now look at the part that came from the **carboxylic acid**. Swap its '-oic acid' ending for 'oate' to get the second bit of the name.

This came from **ethanoic acid**, so it is an **ethanoate**.

3) Put the two parts together.

It's **ethyl ethanoate**
$CH_3COOCH_2CH_3$

~The name's written the opposite way round from the formula.~

This goes for molecules with benzene rings too — react methanol with benzoic acid, and you get methyl **benzoate**, $C_6H_5COOCH_3$.

If either of the carbon chains is **branched** you need to name the attached groups too.
For an ester, number the carbons starting from the C atoms in the C–O–C bond.

1-methylpropyl methanoate
$HCOOCH(CH_3)CH_2CH_3$

ethyl 2-methylbutanoate
$CH_3CH_2CH(CH_3)COOCH_2CH_3$

Esters are Used as Food Flavourings, Perfumes, Solvents and Plasticisers

1) Esters have a **sweet smell** — it varies from gluey sweet for smaller esters to a fruity 'pear drop' smell for the larger ones. This makes them useful in perfumes. The food industry uses esters to **flavour** things like drinks and sweets too.

~The nice fragrances and flavours of lots of flowers and fruits come from esters.~

2) Esters are **polar** liquids so lots of **polar organic compounds** will dissolve in them. They've also got quite **low boiling points**, so they **evaporate easily** from mixtures. This makes them good solvents in **glues** and **printing inks**.

3) Esters are used as **plasticisers** — they're added to plastics during polymerisation to make the plastic more **flexible**. Over time, the plasticiser molecules escape though, and the plastic becomes brittle and stiff.

Practice Questions

Q1 Why is this compound called 3,3,2-trimethylbutanoic acid and not 2,2,3-trimethylbutanoic acid?

Q2 Name the catalyst used in an esterification reaction between an alcohol and a carboxylic acid.

Q3 What properties of esters make them good solvents?

Q4 Name the alcohol and carboxylic acid that can be used to make propyl butanoate.

Exam Questions

1 The structures of substances X and Y are shown on the right:
   a) Write a balanced equation for the reaction between substance X and sodium carbonate, Na_2CO_3. [3 marks]
   b) Substance Y can be synthesised from substance X in a single step process. Give the name of the other reagent necessary for this synthesis and name the type of reaction. [2 marks]

X   Y

2 Ethyl butanoate is an ester that is made by reacting ethanol and butanoic acid.
   a) Draw the structure of ethyl butanoate. [1 mark]
   b) Ethyl butanoate is used as a solvent in some adhesives. Name another possible use for ethyl butanoate. [1 mark]

3 3-methylbutyl ethanoate is the ester responsible for the odour of pear essence.
   a) Write an equation for the formation of this ester from an alcohol and a carboxylic acid. [1 mark]
   b) Name the carboxylic acid used. [1 mark]
   c) What conditions would be needed for this reaction? [2 marks]

Ahh... the sweet smell of success...

I bet your apple-flavoured sweets have never been near a nice rosy apple — it's all the work of esters. And for that matter, I reckon prawn cocktail crisps have never met a prawn, or a cocktail either. None of it's real. And as for potatoes... But maybe nothing is real. Perhaps you're just a mind in a jar, being conned by an evil genius into thinking things are real.

More on Esters

OK, brace yourself. There's some pure unadulterated lard coming up.

Esters are **Hydrolysed** to Form **Alcohols**

Hydrolysis is when a substance is split up by water — but using just water is often really slow, so an **acid** or an **alkali** is often used to speed it up. There are two types of hydrolysis of esters — **acid hydrolysis** and **base hydrolysis**. With both types you get an **alcohol**, but the second product in each case is different.

ACID HYDROLYSIS

Acid hydrolysis splits the ester into an **acid** and an **alcohol** — it's the reverse of the reaction on page 30.

You have to **reflux** the ester with a **dilute acid**, such as hydrochloric or sulfuric. For example:

> As it's a reversible reaction, you need to use lots of water to push the equilibrium over to the right.

ethyl ethanoate   ethanoic acid   ethanol

BASE HYDROLYSIS

This time you have to **reflux** the ester with a **dilute alkali**, such as sodium hydroxide. You get a **carboxylate ion** and an **alcohol**. For example:

ethyl ethanoate   ethanoate   ethanol

Fats and **Oils** are Esters of **Glycerol** and **Fatty Acids**

Fatty acids are long chain **carboxylic acids**. They combine with glycerol (propane-1,2,3-triol) to make fats and oils. The fatty acids can be **saturated** (no double bonds) or **unsaturated** (with C=C double bonds).

Most of a fat or oil is made from fatty acid chains — so it's these that give them many of their properties.

- **'Fats'** have mainly **saturated** hydrocarbon chains — they fit neatly together, increasing the van der Waals forces between them. This means higher temperatures are needed to melt them and they're **solid** at room temperature.

- **'Oils'** have unsaturated hydrocarbon chains — the double bonds mean the chains are bent and don't pack together well, decreasing the effect of the van der Waals forces. So they're easier to melt and are **liquids** at room temperature.

Oils and Fats can be **Hydrolysed** to Make **Glycerol**, **Soap** and **Fatty Acids**

Like any ester, you can **hydrolyse** oils and fats by heating them with **sodium hydroxide**.

And you'll never guess what the sodium salt produced is — **a soap**.

fat   glycerol   sodium salt (soap)

Next, you can convert the sodium salt to a **fatty acid** by adding an acid such as HCl.

$$CH_3(CH_2)_{16}COO^-Na^+ + H^+ \rightarrow CH_3(CH_2)_{16}COOH + Na^+$$
sodium salt (soap)   fatty acid

More on Esters

Biodiesel is a Mixture of Methyl Esters of Fatty Acids

1) Vegetable oils, e.g. rapeseed oil, make good vehicle fuels, but you can't burn them directly in engines.
2) The oils must be converted into **biodiesel** first. This involves reacting them with **methanol**, using **potassium hydroxide** as a **catalyst**.
3) You get a mixture of **methyl esters** of fatty acids — this is biodiesel.

Biodiesel isn't Usually 100% Carbon Neutral

1) Biodiesel can be thought of as **carbon neutral**, because when crops grow they absorb the same amount of CO_2 as they produce when they're burned.
2) But it's not quite as simple as that — energy is **used** to make the fertilizer to grow the crops, and it's used in planting, harvesting and converting the oil. If this energy comes from fossil fuels, then the process **won't** be carbon neutral overall.

Practice Questions

Q1 Describe two different ways of hydrolysing an ester to make an alcohol.
Q2 Draw the structure of a fat.
Q3 What two products do you get when you hydrolyse an oil or fat with sodium hydroxide?
Q4 What does biodiesel consist of?

Exam Questions

1 Compound C, shown on the right, is found in raspberries.

   a) Name compound C. [1 mark]

   b) Draw and name the structures of the products formed when compound C is refluxed with dilute sulfuric acid. What kind of reaction is this? [5 marks]

   c) If compound C is refluxed with excess sodium hydroxide, a similar reaction occurs. What is the difference between the products formed in this reaction and the products of the reaction described in b)? [1 mark]

2 When a vegetable oil was refluxed with concentrated aqueous sodium hydroxide, the products were propane-1,2,3-triol and a salt.

   a) Draw the structure of propane-1,2,3-triol. [1 mark]

   b) The salt was treated with an excess of hydrochloric acid, and oleic acid, $CH_3(CH_2)_7CH=CH(CH_2)_7COOH$, was produced. Write an equation for the formation of this acid from its salt. [1 mark]

   c) Describe a simple chemical test that you could use to distinguish a solution of oleic acid from a solution of $CH_3(CH_2)_{16}COOH$. [2 marks]

Sodium salts — it's all good, clean fun...

I bet you never knew that you could get from something you fry your chips in to something you wash your hands with in one small leap. There are lots of yukkily-complicated structures to learn on these pages — you might find it easier if you think through where the ester breaks in each case and where the atoms of the other reactant add on. Keep at it...

Acyl Chlorides

Acyl chlorides are easy to make and are good starting points for making other types of molecule.

Acyl Chlorides have the Functional Group –COCl

Acyl (or acid) chlorides have the functional group **COCl** — their general formula is $C_nH_{2n-1}OCl$.
All their names end in **–oyl chloride**.

ethanoyl chloride   4-hydroxy-2,3-dimethylpentanoyl chloride

The carbon atoms are numbered from the end with the acyl functional group. (This is the same as with carboxylic acids.)

Acyl Chlorides Easily Lose Their Chlorine

Acyl chlorides react with...

...WATER
A **vigorous** reaction with cold water, producing a **carboxylic acid**.

ethanoyl chloride   ethanoic acid

...ALCOHOLS
A **vigorous** reaction at room temperature, producing an **ester**.

ethanoyl chloride   methyl ethanoate

This irreversible reaction is a much easier, faster way to produce an ester than esterification (page 30).

...AMMONIA
A **violent** reaction at room temperature, producing an **amide**.

ethanoyl chloride   ethanamide

See pages 39 to 41 for amines and amides.

...AMINES
A **violent** reaction at room temperature, producing an **N-substituted amide**.

ethanoyl chloride   N-methylethanamide

Each time, **Cl** is **substituted** by an oxygen or nitrogen group and misty fumes of **hydrogen chloride** are given off.

Acyl Chlorides and Acid Anhydrides React in the Same Way

An **acid anhydride** is made from two identical carboxylic acid molecules. If you know the name of the carboxylic acid, they're easy to name — just take away '**acid**' and add '**anhydride**'.

ethanoic acid   ethanoic anhydride

You need to know the reactions of **water**, **alcohol**, **ammonia** and **amines** with acid anhydrides. Luckily, they're almost the same as those of acyl chlorides — the reactions are just **less vigorous** and you get a **carboxylic acid** formed instead of HCl.

e.g. $(CH_3CO)_2O_{(l)} + H_2O_{(l)} \rightarrow 2CH_3COOH_{(aq)}$
ethanoic anhydride + water → ethanoic acid

Acyl Chlorides

Acyl Chloride Reactions are Nucleophilic Addition-Elimination

In acyl chlorides, both the chlorine and the oxygen atoms draw electrons **towards** themselves, so the carbon has a slight **positive** charge — meaning it's easily attacked by **nucleophiles**.

Here's the mechanism for a **nucleophilic addition-elimination** reaction between ethanoyl chloride and methanol:

Methanol is the nucleophile here. It attacks the partially positive carbon on the acyl chloride, and a pair of electrons from the C=O bond are transferred to the oxygen.

Now the pair of electrons on the oxygen reform the double bond and the chlorine's kicked off.

The chlorine now bonds with the hydrogen in the hydroxyl group...

...and hydrogen chloride's eliminated.

The other reactions of acyl chlorides that you need to know all work in exactly the same way.

You just need to change the nucleophile to water (H_2O:), ammonia ($\ddot{N}H_3$) or an amine (e.g. $CH_3\ddot{N}H_2$).

Ethanoic Anhydride is Used for the Manufacture of Aspirin

Aspirin is an **ester** — it's made by reacting **salicylic acid** (which has an alcohol group) with **ethanoic anhydride** or **ethanoyl chloride**.

Ethanoic anhydride is used in industry because:

- it's **cheaper** than ethanoyl chloride.
- it's **safer** to use than ethanoyl chloride as it's **less corrosive**, reacts **more slowly** with water, and **doesn't** produce dangerous **hydrogen chloride** fumes.

salicylic acid   ethanoic anhydride   aspirin   ethanoic acid

Practice Questions

Q1 Write the equation for the reaction between ethanoyl chloride and ammonia.

Q2 Draw the structure of ethanoic anhydride.

Q3 What part of an acyl chloride is attacked by nucleophiles?

Q4 Give TWO reasons why ethanoic anhydride is preferred to ethanoyl chloride when producing aspirin.

Exam Questions

1   Ethanoyl chloride and ethanoic anhydride both react with methanol.
    a) Write equations for both reactions and name the organic product that is formed in both reactions.   [3 marks]
    b) Give an observation that could be made for the reaction with ethanoyl chloride that would not occur with ethanoic anhydride.   [1 mark]
    c) Ethanoic acid can also be used with methanol to prepare the organic product named in (a). Give one advantage of using ethanoyl chloride.   [1 mark]

2   Ethanoyl chloride and ethylamine react together at room temperature.
    a) Write an equation for this reaction and name the organic product.   [2 marks]
    b) Draw a mechanism for this reaction.   [4 marks]

Anhydrides — aren't they some sort of alien robot...

I could easily lose my mind doing this stuff, let alone a little chlorine particle, and what's worse is I think all those hydrogen chloride fumes are getting to me... I feel kind of dizzy... my head hurts... and I want to lie down and sleep... can't.. keep.. eyes... open... zzzzzzzzzzzzzzzzzzzzzzzzzzzzzzzzzzz...

Aromatic Compounds

Yep, it's another section of organic chemistry, I'm afraid — and it kicks off with the beautiful benzene ring.

Aromatic Compounds are Derived from Benzene

Aliphatic hydrocarbons have no rings of carbon atoms.

Arenes or **aromatic compounds** contain a **benzene ring**.
They're named in two ways. There isn't an easy rule — you just have to learn these examples:

Some are named as substituted benzene rings...

chlorobenzene   nitrobenzene   1, 3-dimethylbenzene

...while others are named as compounds with a phenyl group (C_6H_5) attached.

phenol   2-methylphenol   phenylamine

Benzene has a Ring Of Carbon Atoms

Benzene has the formula C_6H_6. It has a cyclic structure as its six carbon atoms are joined together in a ring. There are two ways of representing it — the **Kekulé model** and **delocalised model**.

The Kekulé Model Came First

The Kekulé Structure

make sure the single and double bonds alternate

or

1) This was proposed by German chemist Friedrich August Kekulé in 1865. He came up with the idea of a **ring** of C atoms with **alternating single** and **double** bonds between them.

2) He later adapted the model to say that the benzene molecule was constantly **flipping** between two forms (**isomers**) by switching over the double and single bonds.

3) If the Kekulé model was correct, you'd expect there to always be three bonds with the length of a **C–C bond** (147 pm) and three bonds with the length of a **C=C bond** (135 pm).

4) However **X-ray diffraction studies** have shown that all the carbon-carbon bonds in benzene have the **same length** — (140 pm) so they're **between** the length of a single bond and a double bond.

5) So the Kekulé structure **can't** be quite right, but it's still used today as it's useful for drawing reaction mechanisms.

The Delocalised Model Replaced Kekulé's Model

The bond-length observations are explained by the delocalised model.

1) In this model, each carbon donates an electron from its **p-orbital**. These electrons combine to form a ring of **delocalised electrons**.

2) All the bonds in the ring are the same, so they are the **same length**.

3) The electrons in the rings are said to be **delocalised** because they don't belong to a specific carbon atom. They are represented as a circle in the ring of carbons rather than as double or single bonds

The Delocalised Structure

or

delocalised ring of electrons

electrons in p-orbitals

delocalised ring of electrons

carbon

hydrogen

Benzene is a planar (flat) molecule — it's got a ring of carbon atoms with their hydrogens sticking out all on a flat plane.

Aromatic Compounds

Enthalpy Changes *Give More Evidence for* Delocalisation

1) Cyclohexene has **one** double bond. When it's hydrogenated, the enthalpy change is **–120 kJmol⁻¹**. If benzene had three double bonds (as in the Kekulé structure), you'd expect it to have an enthalpy of hydrogenation of –360 kJmol⁻¹.

2) But the **experimental** enthalpy of hydrogenation of benzene is **–208 kJmol⁻¹** — far **less exothermic** than expected.

3) Energy is put in to break bonds and released when bonds are made. So **more energy** must have been put in to break the bonds in benzene than would be needed to break the bonds in the Kekulé structure.

4) This difference indicates that benzene is **more stable** than the Kekulé structure would be. This is thought to be due to the **delocalised ring of electrons**.

$$\text{cyclohexene} + H_2 \longrightarrow \quad \Delta H^{\ominus}_{hydrogenation} = -120 \text{ kJmol}^{-1}$$

$$\text{Kekulé structure of benzene} + 3H_2 \longrightarrow$$
$$\text{predicted } \Delta H^{\ominus}_{hydrogenation} = -360 \text{ kJmol}^{-1}$$
$$\text{actual } \Delta H^{\ominus}_{hydrogenation} = -208 \text{ kJmol}^{-1}$$

See pages 61-65 for more on enthalpies.

Arenes Undergo Electrophilic Substitution *Reactions*

The benzene ring is a region of **high electron density**, so it attracts **electrophiles**. As the benzene ring's so stable, it tends to undergo **electrophilic substitution** reactions, which preserve the delocalised ring.

You need to know two **electrophilic substitution mechanisms** for benzene — **Friedel-Crafts acylation** (shown below) and the **nitration reaction** on the next page.

Friedel-Crafts Acylation *Reactions Produce* Phenylketones

Many **useful** chemicals such as **dyes** and **pharmaceuticals** contain benzene rings, but because benzene is so **stable**, it's fairly **unreactive**. **Friedel-Crafts acylation** reactions are used to add an **acyl group** (**–C(=O)–R**) to the benzene ring. Once an acyl group has been added, the side chains can be modified by **further reactions** to produce **useful products**.

An electrophile has to have a pretty strong **positive charge** to be able to attack the stable benzene ring — most just **aren't polarised enough**. But some can be made into **stronger electrophiles** using a catalyst called a **halogen carrier**. Friedel-Crafts acylation uses an **acyl chloride** (see page 34) as an electrophile and a **halogen carrier** such as AlCl₃.

Here's how the AlCl₃ makes the acyl chloride electrophile stronger:

AlCl₃ accepts a **lone pair of electrons** from the acyl chloride. As the lone pair of electrons is pulled away, the **polarisation** in the acyl chloride **increases** and it forms a **carbocation**. This makes it a much, much **stronger electrophile**, and gives it a strong enough charge to **react** with the **benzene ring**.

$$R-C \overset{\delta+}{\underset{\delta-}{\overset{\displaystyle O}{\Vert}}} Cl: \dashrightarrow AlCl_3 \longrightarrow R-C^+ \; AlCl_4^-$$

acyl chloride   halogen carrier   carbocation

And here's how the electrophile is substituted into the benzene ring. The mechanism has **two steps**:

1) **Electrons** in the benzene ring are **attracted** to the positively charged **carbocation**. Two electrons from the benzene **bond** with the carbocation. This **partially breaks** the delocalised ring and gives it a **positive charge**.

2) The **negatively charged AlCl₄⁻** ion is attracted to the **positively charged ring**. One **chloride ion** breaks away from the aluminium chloride ion and **bonds** with the **hydrogen** ion. This **removes the hydrogen** from the ring forming **HCl**. It also allows the catalyst to reform.

The reactants need to be **heated under reflux** in a **non-aqueous** environment for the reaction to occur.

Aromatic Compounds

Nitration is Used in the Manufacture of Explosives and Dyes

When you warm **benzene** with **concentrated nitric** and **sulfuric acids**, you get **nitrobenzene**.
Sulfuric acid acts as a **catalyst** — it helps to make the nitronium ion, NO_2^+, which is the electrophile.

$$HNO_3 + H_2SO_4 \rightarrow H_2NO_3^+ + HSO_4^- \implies H_2NO_3^+ \rightarrow NO_2^+ + H_2O$$

Now here's the electrophilic substitution mechanism:

This mechanism's really similar to the one for Friedel-Crafts acylation on the previous page.

The nitronium ion attacks the benzene ring.

An unstable intermediate forms.

The H$^+$ ion is lost.

This H+ ion reacts with HSO_4^- to reform the catalyst, H_2SO_4.

If you only want one NO_2 group added (**mononitration**), you need to keep the temperature **below 55 °C**.
Above this temperature you'll get lots of substitutions.

Nitration reactions are really useful

1) Nitro compounds can be **reduced** to form **aromatic amines** (see page 39).
   These are used to manufacture **dyes** and **pharmaceuticals**.

2) Nitro compounds **decompose violently** when heated, so they are used
   as **explosives** — such as 2,4,6-trinitromethylbenzene (**trinitrotoluene** — TNT).

Practice Questions

Q1 Explain why electrophiles are attracted to benzene.

Q2 Which halogen carrier is used in the Friedel-Crafts acylation reaction?

Q3 What is used as a catalyst in the nitration of benzene?

Q4 What type of compound is this?

Exam Questions

1   Use the data to explain why it is believed that benzene
    does not have the Kekulé structure.

$\text{cyclohexene} + H_2 \rightarrow \text{cyclohexane} \quad \Delta H = -120 \text{ kJ mol}^{-1}$

$\text{benzene} + 3H_2 \rightarrow \text{cyclohexane} \quad \Delta H = -208 \text{ kJ mol}^{-1}$ [2 marks]

2   $AlCl_3$ is used as a catalyst in the acylation reaction between benzene and ethanoyl chloride.
    a) Describe the conditions for the reaction.   [2 marks]
    b) Draw the structure of the electrophile.   [1 mark]
    c) Draw a dot-cross diagram of the aluminium chloride molecule, $AlCl_3$.   [1 mark]
    d) What feature of the molecule makes it possible for $AlCl_3$ to accept Cl^-?   [1 mark]

3   An electrophilic substitution reaction of benzene is summarised in the diagram:
    a) Name the product A, and the reagents B and C, and give the conditions D.   [4 marks]
    b) Outline a mechanism for this reaction.   [3 marks]
    c) Write equations to show the formation of the electrophile.   [2 marks]

benzene $\xrightarrow[D]{B+C}$ A

Everyone needs a bit of stability in their life...

*The structure of benzene is exceedingly odd — even top scientists struggled to find out what its molecular structure
looked like. If you're asked why benzene reacts in the way it does, it's bound to be something to do with the ring of
delocalised electrons. Remember there's a hydrogen at every point on the benzene ring — it's easy to forget they're there.*

Amines Mainly

This is a-mean, fishy-smelling topic...

Amines are Organic Derivatives of **Ammonia**

If one or more of the **hydrogens** in **ammonia** (NH_3) is replaced with an organic group, you get an **amine**.

If **one** hydrogen is **replaced** with an organic group, you get a **primary amine** — if **two** are replaced, it's a **secondary amine**, **three** means it's a **tertiary amine** and if all **four** are replaced it's called a **quaternary ammonium ion**.

$H_3C-N\overset{H}{\underset{H}{}}$	$H_3C-N\overset{H}{\underset{CH_3}{}}$	$H_3C-N\overset{CH_3}{\underset{CH_3}{}}$	$H_3C-\overset{CH_3}{\underset{CH_3}{N^+}}-CH_3$	
methylamine	dimethylamine	trimethylamine	tetramethylamine ion	phenylamine
(primary amine)	(secondary amine)	(tertiary amine)	(quaternary ammonium ion)	(primary amine)

aliphatic amines

aromatic amine

Because quaternary ammonium ions are **positively charged**, they will hang around with any negative ions that are near. The complexes formed are called **quaternary ammonium salts** — like **tetramethylammonium chloride** (($CH_3)_4N^+Cl^-$). **Small amines** smell similar to **ammonia**, with a **slightly 'fishy'** twist. **Larger amines** smell very '**fishy**'. (Nice.)

Quaternary Ammonium Salts are Used as **Cationic Surfactants**

Cationic surfactants are used in things like **fabric conditioners** and **hair products**. They are **quaternary ammonium salts** with at least one long hydrocarbon chain.

The **positively charged** part (ammonium ion) will bind to negatively charged surfaces such as hair and fibre. This gets rid of **static**.

An Amine Has a **Lone Pair of Electrons** That Can Form **Dative Covalent Bonds**

1) Amines act as **bases** because they **accept protons**. There's a **lone pair of electrons** on the **nitrogen** atom that forms a **dative covalent (coordinate) bond** with an H^+ ion.

2) The **strength** of the **base** depends on how **available** the nitrogen's lone pair of electrons is. The more **available** the **lone pair** is, the more likely the amine is to **accept a proton**, and the **stronger** a base it will be. A **lone pair** of electrons will be **more available** if its **electron density** is **higher**.

3) **Primary aliphatic amines** are **stronger** bases than **ammonia**, which is a **stronger** base than **aromatic amines**. Here's why:

The more **available** the lone pair of electrons, the **stronger** the base...

Greater availability of lone pair of electrons

Stronger bases

primary aromatic amine (phenylamine)

ammonia

primary aliphatic amine

= distribution of negative charge

The benzene ring draws electrons towards itself and the nitrogen's lone pair gets partially delocalised onto the ring. So the electron density on the nitrogen decreases. This makes the lone pair much less available.

Alkyl groups push electrons onto attached groups. So the electron density on the nitrogen atom increases. This makes the lone pair more available.

Amines Mainly

You know what amines are, you know they act as bases and that they turn up in conditioner — but how are they made?

Aliphatic Amines are made from Haloalkanes or Nitriles

There are **two** ways to produce aliphatic amines — either from **haloalkanes** or by **reducing nitriles**.
The method for producing **aromatic amines** is different again — as you'll see on the next page.

YOU CAN HEAT A HALOALKANE WITH AMMONIA

Amines can be made by heating a **haloalkane** with **excess ammonia**.

E.g.

$$2\ NH_3 + CH_3CH_2Br \longrightarrow CH_3CH_2NH_2 + NH_4Br$$

ammonia   ethylamine

You'll get a **mixture** of primary, secondary and tertiary amines, and quaternary ammonium salts, as more than one hydrogen is likely to be substituted.

You can separate the products using **fractional distillation**.

You need to know the mechanism for this reaction:

Ammonia attacks the carbon in the haloalkane

The halogen is released

ammonia + haloalkane   ⟶   alkylammonium salt   ...then...

A second ammonia molecule donates its lone pair of electrons to a hydrogen, which breaks off from the alkylammonium salt.

alkylammonium salt ⇌ primary amine + ammonium salt

As long as there's some more of the haloalkane, **further substitutions** can take place. They keep happening until you get a **quaternary ammonium salt**, which can't react any further as it has no lone pair of electrons.

Amines undergo the same mechanism as ammonia (see above).

primary amine →(haloalkane)→ secondary amine →(haloalkane)→ tertiary amine →(haloalkane)→ quaternary ammonium ion

OR YOU CAN REDUCE A NITRILE

You can reduce a nitrile to an amine using **LiAlH₄** (a strong reducing agent), followed by some **dilute acid**. Another way is to reflux the nitrile with **sodium** metal and **ethanol**.

E.g.

$$CH_3C{\equiv}N + 4[H] \xrightarrow[\text{(2) dilute acid}]{\text{(1) LiAlH}_4} CH_3CH_2NH_2$$

ethanenitrile   ethylamine

I can't afford LiAlH₄...

Becky was reduced to tears by lithium aluminium hydride.

These are great in the lab, but LiAlH₄ and sodium are too **expensive** for industrial use.

Industry uses a **metal catalyst** such as platinum or nickel at a high temperature and pressure — it's called **catalytic hydrogenation**.

$$CH_3C{\equiv}N + 2H_2 \xrightarrow[\text{high temp. \& pressure}]{\text{Ni}} CH_3CH_2NH_2$$

ethanenitrile   ethylamine

Amines Mainly

Aromatic Amines are made by Reducing a Nitro Compound

Aromatic amines are produced by **reducing** a nitro compound, such as **nitrobenzene**.
There are **two steps** to the method:

1) First you need to heat a mixture of a **nitro compound**,
tin metal and **concentrated hydrochloric acid** under **reflux**
— this makes a salt. For example, if you use nitrobenzene,
the salt formed is $C_6H_5NH_3^+Cl^-$.

2) Then to turn the salt into an **aromatic amine**, you need
to add an alkali, such as **sodium hydroxide** solution.

And now for a weeny bit about amides...

Amides are Carboxylic Acid Derivatives

Amides contain the functional group **–CONH$_2$**.
The **carbonyl group** pulls electrons away from the NH$_2$
group, so amides behave differently from amines.

amide   N-substituted amide   one of the hydrogens is replaced with an alkyl group

Practice Questions

Q1 Explain how amines and ammonia can form dative (co-ordinate) covalent bonds.

Q2 Explain why amines and ammonia can act as nucleophiles.

Q3 What conditions are needed to reduce nitrobenzene to phenylamine?

Q4 Haloalkanes react with amines to produce a mixture of primary, secondary and tertiary amines.
How can they be separated?

Exam Questions

1   a)   Explain how methylamine, CH_3NH_2, can act as a base.   [1 mark]
    b)   Methylamine is a stronger base than ammonia, NH_3. However, phenylamine, $C_6H_5NH_2$, is a weaker
         base than ammonia. Explain these differences in base strength.   [4 marks]

2   The reaction between an amine and a haloalkane produces a mixture of products.
    a)   Write an equation for the formation of a quaternary ammonium salt from ethylamine and bromomethane. [2 marks]
    b)   What condition would help to ensure that the quaternary ammonium salt would be a major product?   [1 mark]
    c)   Name a use for quaternary ammonium salts.   [1 mark]

3   a)   Propylamine can be synthesised from bromopropane.
         Suggest a disadvantage of this synthesis route.   [1 mark]
    b)   Propylamine can also be synthesised from propanenitrile.
         (i) Suggest suitable reagents for its preparation in a laboratory.   [2 marks]
         (ii) Why is this method not suitable for industrial use?   [1 mark]
         (iii) What reagents and conditions are used in industry?   [2 marks]

4   Ethylamine can react with bromoethane to form a compound of molecular formula $C_4H_{11}N$.
    a)   Write an equation for the reaction and name the organic product.   [2 marks]
    b)   Name and outline a mechanism for the reaction.   [4 marks]

You've got to learn it — amine it might come up in your exam...

*Rotting fish smells so bad because the flesh releases diamines as it decomposes. Is it fish that smells of amines or amines
that smell of fish — it's one of those chicken or egg things that no one can answer. Well, enough philosophical pondering
— we all know the answer to the meaning of life. It's 42. Now make sure you know the answers to the questions above.*

Amino Acids and Proteins

Wouldn't it be nice if you could go to sleep with this book under your pillow and when you woke up you'd know it all.

Amino Acids have an Amino Group and a Carboxyl Group

An amino acid has a **basic amino group** (NH$_2$) and an **acidic carboxyl group** (COOH). This makes them **amphoteric** — they've got both acidic and basic properties.

They're **chiral molecules** because the carbon has **four** different groups attached. So a solution of a single amino acid enantiomer will **rotate polarised light** — see page 26.

Glycine's the exception to this as its R group is just a hydrogen.

Amino Acids Have Common and Systematic Names

Amino acids often have a **common** and a **systematic name**. You just have to **learn** the common names, but you can **work out** the systematic names.

Systematic naming

1) Find the **longest carbon chain** that includes the carboxylic acid group and write down its name.

2) **Number the carbons** in the chain starting with the carbon in the carboxylic acid group as number 1.

3) Write down the **positions of any NH$_2$ groups** and show that they are NH$_2$ groups with the word '**amino**'.

propanoic acid

2-aminopropanoic acid
(alanine is its common name)

Amino Acids Can Exist As Zwitterions

A zwitterion is a **dipolar ion** — it has both a **positive** and a **negative charge** in different parts of the molecule. Zwitterions only exist near an amino acid's **isoelectric point**. This is the **pH** where the **average overall charge** on the amino acid is zero. It's different for different amino acids — it depends on their R-group.

In conditions more **acidic** than the isoelectric point, the –NH$_2$ group is likely to be **protonated**.

At the isoelectric point, both the carboxyl group and the amino group are likely to be ionised — forming an ion called a **zwitterion**.

In conditions more **basic** than the isoelectric point, the –COOH group is likely to **lose** its proton.

low pH

zwitterion

high pH

Paper Chromatography is used to Separate Out a Mixture of Amino Acids

If you have a solution containing a **mixture** of amino acids, you can use **paper chromatography** to **separate** them out and **identify** the different amino acids that make up your solution.

1) Draw a **pencil line** near the bottom of a piece of chromatography paper and put a **concentrated spot** of the mixture of amino acids on it.

2) Dip the bottom of the paper (not the spot) into a solvent.

3) As the solvent spreads up the paper, the different amino acids move with it, but at **different rates**, so they separate out.

4) You can **identify** each amino acid by comparing how far it moves to how far the solvent moves.

5) Amino acids aren't coloured — so you have to spray **ninhydrin solution** on the paper to turn them purple.

distance moved by solvent ('solvent front')

spot of pigment

solvent

point of origin

Amino Acids and Proteins

Proteins are Condensation Polymers of Amino Acids

Proteins are made up of **lots** of amino acids joined together by **peptide links**. The chain is put together by **condensation** reactions and broken apart by **hydrolysis** reactions.

Here's how two amino acids join together to make a **dipeptide**:

Lots of these reactions would happen to make a long chain.

Proteins are really polyamides — the monomers are joined by amide groups. In proteins these are called peptide links.

To break up the protein (**hydrolyse** it) you need to use pretty harsh conditions. **Hot aqueous 6 M hydrochloric acid** is added, and the mixture is heated under reflux for 24 hours. The final mixture is then neutralised.

Hydrogen Bonds Help Keep Proteins in Shape

1) Proteins are **not** just straight chains of amino acids. Instead, the chains **fold** or **twist** due to **intermolecular forces**.

2) **Hydrogen bonding** is one type of force that holds proteins in shape. Hydrogen bonds exist between polar groups — e.g. –OH and –NH_2.

3) Their 3-dimensional shape is **vital** to how proteins **function**. For example, changing the shape of a protein that acts as an **enyzme** can stop it working.

4) Factors such as **heat** and **pH** can affect hydrogen bonding and so can **change the shape** of proteins.

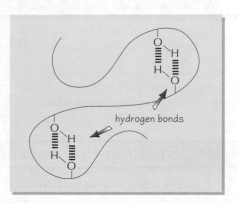

hydrogen bonds

Practice Questions

Q1 Draw the structure of a typical amino acid using R to represent the variable group.

Q2 Draw the zwitterion that would be formed from your amino acid.

Q3 What type of bond links the two amino acids in a dipeptide?

Q4 Outline the role of hydrogen bonds in proteins.

Exam Questions

1 Aspartic acid is an amino acid of molecular formula $C_4H_7O_4N$. It has two carboxylic acid groups and one amine group. The carbon chain is unbranched.
   a) Draw the structure of aspartic acid and label any chiral carbons with an asterisk *. [2 marks]
   b) Give the systematic name for aspartic acid. [1 mark]

2 The diagram on the right shows the structure of an amino acid.
   a) Draw the structure of the zwitterion of this amino acid. [1 mark]
   b) Write an equation showing what happens when an excess of aqueous acid is added to the zwitterion. Draw the structure of the product. [1 mark]

3 The amino acid serine is otherwise known as 2-amino-3-hydroxypropanoic acid.
   a) Draw the structure of serine. [1 mark]
   b) When two amino acids react together, a dipeptide is formed.
      (i) Explain the meaning of the term dipeptide. [2 marks]
      (ii) Draw the structures of the two dipeptides that are formed when serine and glycine react together. The structure of glycine is shown on the right. [2 marks]
   c) The dipeptides formed can be hydrolysed to give the original amino acids again. Give the reagent(s) and conditions for this reaction. [2 marks]

My top three tides of all time — high tide, low tide and peptide...

The word zwitterion is such a lovely word — it flutters off your tongue like a butterfly. This page isn't too painful — another organic structure, a nice experiment and some stuff on proteins. There's even a two-for-the-price-of-one equation — forwards it's condensation; backwards it's hydrolysis. Remember to learn the conditions for the hydrolysis though.

Polymers

Polymers are long molecules made by joining lots of little molecules together. They're made using addition or condensation polymerisation, as you're about to see.

Addition Polymers are Formed from Alkenes

Addition polymerisation is a free radical addition reaction.

The double bonds in alkenes can open up and join together to make long chains called **addition polymers**. It's like they're holding hands in a big line. The individual, small alkenes are called **monomers**.

Poly(phenylethene) is formed from **phenylethene**.

the double bond opens up

'n' means there are lots of these units

This is what a section of the chain would look like.

phenylethene monomer

poly(phenylethene) polymer

section of poly(phenylethene) polymer

Poly(chloroethene) is formed from **chloroethene**.

The names of polymers can be written with or without the brackets — e.g. poly(chloroethene) or polychloroethene.

chloroethene monomer

poly(chloroethene) polymer

Polychloroethene's also known as PVC — Poly(vinyl chloride) or Pretty Vulgar Clothing.

Condensation Polymers Include Polyamides, Polyesters and Polypeptides

1) **Condensation polymerisation** usually involves two different types of monomer.

2) Each monomer has at least **two functional groups**. Each functional group reacts with a group on another monomer to form a link, creating polymer chains.

3) Each time a link is formed, a small molecule is lost (water) — that's why it's called **condensation** polymerisation.

4) Examples of condensation polymers include **polyamides**, **polyesters** and **polypeptides** (or proteins, see page 43).

Reactions Between Dicarboxylic Acids and Diamines Make Polyamides

The **carboxyl** groups of **dicarboxylic acids** react with the **amino** groups of **diamines** to form **amide links**.

a water molecule is eliminated

dicarboxylic acid

diamine

amide link

$+ H_2O$

Dicarboxylic acids and diamines have functional groups at each end of the molecule, so long chains can form.

You need to know how the polyamides **nylon 6,6** and **KEVLAR®** link together.

Example   **Nylon 6,6** — made from **1,6-diaminohexane** and **hexanedioic acid**.

1,6-diaminohexane

hexanedioic acid

nylon 6,6

$+ 2nH_2O$

Example   **KEVLAR®** — made from **benzene-1,4-diamine** and **benzene-1,4-dicarboxylic acid**.

benzene-1,4-diamine

benzene-1,4-dicarboxylic acid

Kevlar

$+ 2nH_2O$

Polymers

Reactions Between *Dicarboxylic Acids* and *Diols* Make *Polyesters*

The **carboxyl** groups of dicarboxylic acids can also react with the **hydroxyl** groups of **diols** to form **ester links**.

Polymers joined by **ester links** are called **polyesters** — an example is **Terylene**.

Example **Terylene (PET)** — formed from **benzene-1,4-dicarboxylic acid** and **ethane-1,2-diol**.

Practice Questions

Q1 What type of polymer is: a) polyethene, b) polyester?

Q2 What molecule is eliminated when a polyester is made?

Q3 Which type of condensation polymer is made when a dicarboxylic acid reacts with a diamine?

Q4 Name an example of a polyester.

Exam Questions

1 The diagram shows three repeating units of a polymer.

   a) Name the polymer. [1 mark]
   b) Name the **type** of polymerisation reaction by which this polymer would be formed. [1 mark]
   c) Write an equation for the formation of this polymer from its monomers. [1 mark]

2 a) Nylon 6,6 is the most commonly produced nylon. A section of the polymer is shown below:

   (i) Draw the structural formulae of the monomers from which nylon 6,6 is formed. It is not necessary to draw the carbon chains out in full. [2 marks]
   (ii) Suggest why this nylon polymer is called nylon 6,6. [1 mark]
   (iii) Give a name for the linkage between the monomers in this polymer. [1 mark]

   b) A polyester is formed by the reaction between the monomers hexanedioic acid and 1,6-hexanediol.
   (i) Draw the repeating unit for the polyester. [1 mark]
   (ii) Explain why this is an example of condensation polymerisation. [1 mark]

Never miss your friends again — form a polymer...

These polymers are really useful — KEVLAR® is used for bulletproof vests and nylon's used for parachutes. And someone had to invent them. Just think, you could be the next mad inventor, working for the biggest secret agency in the world. And you'd have a really fast car, which obviously would turn into a yacht with the press of a button...

More About Polymers

Polymers are amazingly useful. But they have one big drawback...

Polymers — *Useful* but Difficult to *Get Rid Of*

1) Synthetic polymers have loads of **advantages**, so they're incredibly widespread these days — we take them pretty much for granted.

   Just imagine what you'd have to live without ⟹ if there were no polymers...

   (Okay... I could live without the polystyrene head, but the rest of this stuff is pretty useful.)

2) **Addition polymers** such as poly(ethene) and polystyrene are very unreactive. This is an advantage when they are being used — e.g. a polystyrene cup won't react with your coffee, but has the disadvantage of making them **non-biodegradable**.

3) **Condensation polymers** such as PET (a polyester that's used to make fizzy drinks bottles and carrier bags amongst other things) and nylon (a polyamide) can be broken down by **hydrolysis**. This is a reverse of the reaction by which they were made. These polymers are **biodegradable**, although the process is **very slow**.

Waste Plastics Have to be *Disposed Of*

It's estimated that in the UK we throw away over **3 million tons** of plastic (i.e. synthetic polymers) every year. Because plastics either take a **very long time** to biodegrade or are **non-biodegradable**, the question of what to do with all those plastic objects when we've finished using them is an important one.

The options are **burying**, **burning** or sorting for **reusing** or **recycling**. None of these methods is an ideal solution — they all have **advantages** and **disadvantages** associated with them.

```
                    Waste
  burying    ⟵    plastics    ⟶   burning
in landfill                        as fuel
                      ↓
                   sorting
                   ↙     ↘
           remoulding      cracking
               ↓              ↓
             new          processing
            objects        ↙      ↘
                       other      new
                     chemicals  plastics
```

Waste Plastics can be *Buried*

1) **Landfill** is one option for dealing with waste plastics. It is generally used when the plastic is:

   - difficult to separate from other waste,
   - not in sufficient quantities to make separation financially worthwhile,
   - too difficult technically to recycle.

2) Landfill is a relatively **cheap** and **easy** method of waste disposal, but it requires **areas of land**.

3) As the waste decomposes it can release **methane** — a **greenhouse gas**. **Leaks** from landfill sites can also **contaminate water supplies**.

4) The **amount of waste** we generate is becoming more and more of a problem, so there's a need to **reduce** landfill as much as possible.

Waste Plastics can be *Burned*

1) Waste plastics can be **burned** and the heat used to generate **electricity**.

2) This process needs to be carefully **controlled** to reduce **toxic** gases. For example, polymers that contain **chlorine** (such as **PVC**) produce **HCl** when they're burned — this has to be removed.

3) So, waste gases from the combustion are passed through **scrubbers** which can **neutralise** gases such as HCl by allowing them to react with a **base**.

4) But, the waste gases, e.g. carbon dioxide, will still contribute to the **greenhouse effect**.

Rex and Dirk enjoy some waist plastic.

More About Polymers

Waste Plastics can be Recycled

Because many plastics are made from non-renewable **oil-fractions**, it makes sense to recycle plastics as much as possible. There's more than one way to recycle plastics. After **sorting** into different types:

- some plastics (poly(propene), for example) can be **melted** and **remoulded**,
- some plastics can be **cracked** into **monomers**, and these can be used to make more plastics or other chemicals.

> Plastic products are usually marked to make sorting easier. The different numbers show different polymers
> e.g.
> 3 = PVC, and 5 = poly(propene)

Environmental Pressure May Change Our Use of Plastics

Plastics are so **useful** that it's very unlikely we'll stop using them anytime soon, despite the disposal problems. However, **greater awareness** of the problems may change how we use plastics.

> For example, supermarkets have been criticised for the amount of plastic waste they create. They've responded by:
>
> 1) Trying to **reduce** the amount of **plastic packaging** on food items.
> 2) Employing scientists to **develop** plastics that **biodegrade quickly**, e.g. food packaging that biodegrades in just one year.
> 3) Encouraging us to **reuse plastics** by selling 'bags for life' that can be used over and over again or by charging for carrier bags.

Practice Questions

Q1 Why isn't poly(ethene) biodegradable?

Q2 Give one advantage and one disadvantage of burning as a method of disposing of waste plastics.

Q3 Name a polymer that can be melted and remoulded.

Q4 Explain why burning PVC produces HCl gas, but burning poly(ethene) doesn't.

Exam Questions

1   One of the products of burning waste PVC is HCl gas.
The gas can be removed by passing it through scrubbers containing other substances.

a)   Choose a substance from the following list that could be used to neutralise the HCl produced and write an equation for the neutralisation reaction.

$CaCO_3$ NH_4Cl $CH_3COOH.$ [3 marks]

b)   Name an environmental problem that a product of this reaction may contribute to.   [1 mark]

2   The diagram on the right shows sections of two polymers.

a)   Name:
i)   each type of polymer.   [2 marks]
ii) the monomers that each of these polymers is formed from.   [2 marks]

A: $\left[\begin{array}{c} O \\ || \\ C-N-(CH_2)_5 \\ | \\ H \end{array} \begin{array}{c} O \\ || \\ C-N-(CH_2)_5 \\ | \\ H \end{array} \right]$

B: $\left[\begin{array}{c} CH_3 \ H \ CH_3 \ H \\ | \ \ | \ \ | \ \ | \\ C-C-C-C \\ | \ \ | \ \ | \ \ | \\ H \ H \ H \ H \end{array} \right]$

b)   Which of these polymers is biodegradable?   [1 mark]

c)   Give one advantage and one disadvantage of landfill as a disposal method for waste plastic.   [2 marks]

Phil's my recycled plastic plane — but I don't know where to land Phil...

You might have noticed that all this recycling business is a hot topic these days. And not just in the usual places, such as Chemistry books. No, no, no... recycling even makes it regularly onto the news as well. This suits examiners just fine — they like you to know how useful and important chemistry is. So learn this stuff, pass your exam, and do some recycling.

Organic Synthesis and Analysis

In your exam you may be asked to suggest a pathway for the synthesis of a particular molecule. These pages contain a summary of some of the reactions you should know.

Chemists use **Synthesis Routes** to Get from One Compound to Another

Chemists have got to be able to make one compound from another. It's vital for things like **designing medicines**. It's also good for making imitations of **useful natural substances** when the real things are hard to extract.

These reactions are covered elsewhere in the book, or in your AS notes, so check back for extra details.

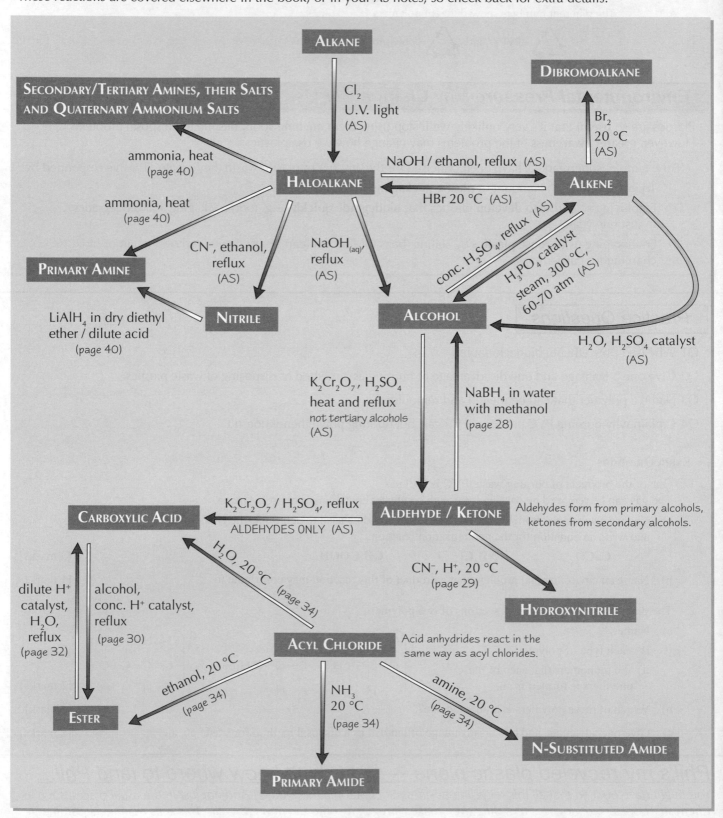

Organic Synthesis and Analysis

Synthesis Route for Making Aromatic Compounds

There are not so many of these reactions to learn — so make sure you know all the itty-bitty details.
If you can't remember any of the reactions, look back to the relevant pages and take a quick peek over them.

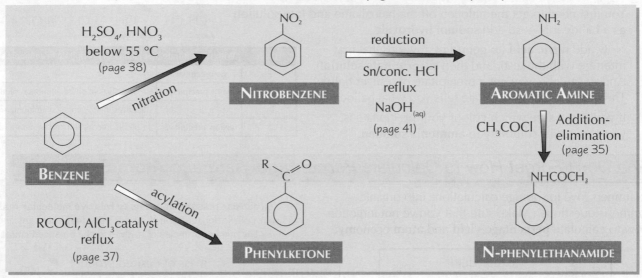

BENZENE

H_2SO_4, HNO_3 below 55 °C (page 38) — nitration → NITROBENZENE (NO_2)

reduction — Sn/conc. HCl reflux — $NaOH_{(aq)}$ (page 41) → AROMATIC AMINE (NH_2)

CH_3COCl — Addition-elimination (page 35) → N-PHENYLETHANAMIDE ($NHCOCH_3$)

RCOCl, $AlCl_3$ catalyst reflux (page 37) — acylation → PHENYLKETONE

Make Sure You Give All The Information

If you're asked how to make one compound from another in the exam, make sure you include:

1) any **special procedures**, such as refluxing.
2) the **conditions** needed, e.g. high temperature or pressure, or the presence of a catalyst.
3) any **safety** precautions, e.g. do it in a fume cupboard.

If there are things like hydrogen chloride or hydrogen cyanide around, you really don't want to go breathing them in. Stuff like bromine and strong acids and alkalis are corrosive, so you don't want to splash them on your bare skin.

Here are a few other bits and bobs you need to know...

You Can Test Whether You've Got a Primary, Secondary or Tertiary Alcohol

To find out which sort of alcohol you've got, you warm it with the **oxidising** agent **acidified potassium dichromate(VI)**.
Then you watch for a colour change...

PRIMARY – the orange dichromate slowly turns green as an **aldehyde** forms (then eventually a carboxylic acid).

SECONDARY – the orange dichromate slowly turns green as a **ketone** forms.

TERTIARY – nothing happens — boring, but easy to remember.

> The colour change is the orange dichromate(VI) ion, $Cr_2O_7{}^{2-}$, being reduced to the green chromium(III) ion, Cr^{3+}.

The test shows the **same result** for **primary** and **secondary** alcohols — you have to perform **another test** to find out if you have produced an aldehyde or a ketone.

You can distinguish between an **aldehyde** and a **ketone** using **Tollens' reagent** (an aldehyde forms a **silver mirror**, **no reaction** with a **ketone**), or with either **Fehling's solution** or **Benedict's solution** (an aldehyde gives a **brick red precipitate**, **no reaction** with a **ketone**).
There's more about these tests on page 28.

Use Bromine to Test for Unsaturation

To see if a compound is unsaturated (contains any double bonds), all you need to do is shake it with **orange bromine solution**.

The solution will quickly **decolourise** if the substance is unsaturated.

bromine water + unsaturated compound → SHAKE → solution goes colourless

Organic Synthesis and Analysis

Use NaOH and Silver Nitrate Solution to Find Out What Haloalkane You've Got

At AS you learned that you could identify **halide ions** using **silver nitrate solution**.
Well, you can use this test to distinguish between different haloalkanes.

X is a halogen

$$CH_3CH_2X + OH^- \rightarrow CH_3CH_2OH + X^-$$

1) You first need to get the halogen off the haloalkane and into solution as a halide ion — so add **sodium hydroxide**.

2) Now add **nitric acid** (to get rid of any ions that may interfere with the test), and then **silver nitrate solution**. And — ta da — you get a precipitate of a silver halide. The **colour** of the precipitate tells you what halide it is.

3) If you're not sure which colour your precipitate is, you can test its solubility in **ammonia solution**.

Halide	With silver nitrate	Solubility of precipitate in ammonia solution
F⁻	no precipitate	—
Cl⁻	white precipitate	dissolves in dilute ammonia solution
Br⁻	cream precipitate	dissolves in concentrated ammonia solution
I⁻	yellow precipitate	insoluble in concentrated ammonia solution

And Don't Forget How to Calculate Percentage Yield and Atom Economy

Examiners love to squidge calculations into organic synthesis questions. Make sure that you've not forgotten how to calculate **percentage yield** and **atom economy**:

You can use **masses in grams** or **relative molecular masses**. In your calculation, use the M_r of each product/reactant, multiplied by the number of moles of it given in the balanced equation.

$$\% \text{ yield} = \frac{\text{actual yield}}{\text{theoretical yield}} \times 100$$

The theoretical yield is how much product you expect to get from the reactants (you can work this out from the balanced equation).

$$\% \text{ atom economy} = \frac{\text{mass of desired product}}{\text{total mass of reactants}} \times 100$$

The atom economy is the proportion of reactant atoms that become part of the desired product. A low atom economy means a reaction is very wasteful — and wasteful reactions aren't sustainable.

Practice Questions

Q1 Give two reagents that when combined with an alcohol will give an ester.
Q2 What type of organic product would be formed from the reaction between a haloalkane and ammonia?
Q3 What reagents are needed to change nitrobenzene into phenylamine?
Q4 Which type of alcohol cannot be oxidised by acidified potassium dichromate?

Exam Questions

1 Describe a chemical test that would distinguish between each of the following pairs of compounds.

a) A (pentagon) B $\overset{H}{\underset{H}{}}C=C\overset{C_3H_7}{\underset{H}{}}$ [3 marks]

b) C $\overset{H}{\underset{H}{}}C=C\overset{CH_2CH_2COCH_3}{\underset{H}{}}$ D $\overset{H}{\underset{H}{}}C=C\overset{CH_2CH_2CHO}{\underset{H}{}}$ [3 marks]

2 The diagram on the right shows a possible reaction pathway for the two-step synthesis of a ketone from a haloalkane.

Haloalkane P $\xrightarrow[\text{NaOH}]{\text{Step 1}}$ Alcohol Q $\xrightarrow{\text{Step 2}}$ Ketone R

a) Give the name of alcohol Q. [1 mark]

Here is the balanced equation for Step 1 of the synthesis: $CH_3CHClCH_3 + NaOH \rightarrow CH_3CH(OH)CH_3 + NaCl$

b) Calculate the % atom economy for the production of Alcohol Q in Step 1. Give your answer to 1 d.p. [3 marks]

c) 24.9 g of Alcohol Q was produced from 39.25 g of Haloalkane P. Calculate the percentage yield of Step 1. [4 marks]

d) Give the other reagents and the conditions needed to carry out Step 2. [2 marks]

3 Ethyl methanoate is one of the compounds responsible for the smell of raspberries.
Outline, with reaction conditions, how it could be synthesised in the laboratory from methanol. [7 marks]

4 How would you synthesise propanol starting with propane? State the reaction conditions and reagents needed for each step and any particular safety considerations. [8 marks]

I saw a farmer turn a tractor into a field once — now that's impressive...

There's loads of information here. Tons and tons of it. But you've covered pretty much all of it before, so it shouldn't be too hard to make sure it's firmly embedded in your head. If it's not, you know what to do — go back over it again. Then cover the diagrams up, and try to draw them out from memory. And then make a table with the tests in.

Mass Spectrometry

A mass spectrometer ionises organic molecules and then breaks lots of the ions up into fragments. Not good news for the molecule, but very handy for scientists. A mass spectrum can tell you the molecular mass, molecular formula, empirical formula, structural formula and your horoscope for the next fortnight.

Mass Spectrometry Can Tell You the M_r of a Compound

1) **Mass spectrometry** can be used to find the **relative molecular mass**, M_r, of a compound.

2) Electrons in the spectrometer **bombard** the sample molecules and **break electrons off**, forming ions. A **mass spectrum** is produced, showing the **relative amounts** of ions with different mass-to-charge ratios.

3) To find the M_r of a compound you look at the **molecular ion peak** (the **M peak**).

4) This peak is due to the molecular ion, which is formed by the loss of **one electron**. E.g. for pentane: $C_5H_{10} \rightarrow [C_5H_{10}]^+ + e^-$

5) The **mass/charge value** of the molecular ion peak is the molecular mass:

Assuming the ion has 1+ charge, which it normally will have.

Here's the mass spectrum of pentane. Its M peak is at 72 — so the compound's M_r is 72.

For most <u>organic compounds</u> the M peak is the one with the second highest mass/charge ratio. The smaller peak to the right of the M peak is called the M+1 peak — it's caused by the presence of the carbon isotope ^{13}C.

The Molecular Ion can be Broken into Smaller Fragments

The bombarding electrons make some of the molecular ions break up into **fragments**. The fragments that are ions show up on the mass spectrum, making a **fragmentation pattern**. Fragmentation patterns can be used to identify **molecules** and even their **structures**.

Fragment (consider revising)

Mr Clippy's grammar advice also applies to chemistry.

For propane, the molecular ion is $CH_3CH_2CH_3^+$, and the fragments it breaks into include CH_3^+ ($M_r = 15$) and $CH_3CH_2^+$ ($M_r = 29$).

Only the **ions** show up on the mass spectrum — the **free radicals** are 'lost'.

$CH_3CH_2CH_3^+$
$CH_3CH_2 \bullet$ free radical $+ CH_3^+$ ion
$CH_3CH_2^+$ ion $+ \bullet CH_3$ free radical

To work out the structural formula, you've got to work out what **ion** could have made each peak from its **m/z value**. (You assume that the m/z value of a peak matches the **mass** of the ion that made it.)

Example

Use this mass spectrum to work out the structure of the molecule:

It's only the m/z values you're interested in — ignore the heights of the bars for now.

Some common groups to look for:

Fragment	Molecular Mass
CH_3	15
C_2H_5	29
C_3H_7	43
OH	17

1. Identify the fragments

This molecule's got a peak at 15 m/z, so it's likely to have a CH_3 **group**.

It's also got a peak at 17 m/z, so it's likely to have an **OH group**.

Other ions are matched to the peaks here:

2. Piece them together to form a molecule with the correct M_r

Ethanol has all the fragments on this spectrum.

Ethanol's **molecular mass** is 46. This should be the same as the m/z value of the M peak — it is.

Mass Spectrometry

More *Stable* Fragments Give *Higher Peaks*

1) Some fragment ions are **more stable** than others, so they're more likely to form.
   That means they'll be more abundant, and will have **higher peaks** on the mass spectrum.

2) The mass spectrum of ethanol on the previous page shows that the **most abundant peak**
   (the one with the highest bar) has a mass of **31** — this represents the fragment ion CH_2OH^+.

3) Two very stable fragment ions are **carbocations** and **acylium ions** — you'd expect high peaks for them.

A carbocation is an ion with a **positively charged carbon**. Carbocations are relatively stable ions because alkyl groups feed **electrons** towards the positive charge. Carbocations with more alkyl groups are more stable.

Alkyl groups are alkanes with a hydrogen removed, e.g. methyl, CH_3.

🔲 = alkyl group
➤ = electron donation

primary carbocation (one 🔲 group)

secondary carbocation (two 🔲 groups)

tertiary carbocation (three 🔲 groups)

Least Stable ⟶ Most Stable

The **acylium ion** (RCO^+) is often formed from aliphatic ketones.
It has the resonance forms:

$$R - C \equiv \overset{\oplus}{\underset{..}{O}} \longleftrightarrow R - \overset{\oplus}{C} \equiv \underset{..}{O}$$

If a molecule has resonance forms, it changes between them very quickly.

Resonating between two or more different structures helps **stabilise** what would otherwise be an unstable ion.
So there's a good chance that a tall peak at m/z = **43** will be CH_3CO^+, and one at m/z = **57** will be $CH_3CH_2CO^+$.
As long as you could get such a fragment from the molecule — a peak at 43 may also be $C_3H_7^+$.

Use the *M+1 Peak* to Work Out the *Number* of *Carbon Atoms* in a Molecule

The peak **1 unit** to the right of the M peak is called the **M+1 peak**. It's mostly due to the **carbon-13 isotope** which exists naturally and makes up about 1.1% of carbon.

You can use the M+1 peak to find out **how many carbon atoms** there are in the molecule.
There's even a handy formula for this (as long as the molecule's not too huge):

$$\frac{\text{height of M+1 peak}}{\text{height of M peak}} \times 100 = \text{number of carbon atoms in compound}$$

EXAMPLE

If a molecule has a molecular peak with a relative abundance of 44.13%, and an M+1 peak with a relative abundance of 1.41%, how many carbon atoms does it contain?

$(1.41 \div 44.13) \times 100 = 3.195$ So the molecule contains 3 carbon atoms.

An *M+2 Peak* Tells Us the Compound Contains *Chlorine* or *Bromine*

If a molecule's got either **chlorine** or **bromine** in it you'll get an **M+2 peak** as well as an M peak and an M+1 peak.
It's because chlorine and bromine have natural isotopes with different masses and they all show up on the spectrum.

Chlorine's two isotopes, **Cl-35** and **Cl-37**, occur in the ratio of **3:1**.

So if a molecule contains chlorine, it will give an **M peak** and an **M+2 peak** with heights in the ratio **3:1**.

Bromine's got two isotopes, **Br-79** and **Br-81**, that occur in **equal amounts**.
So if a molecule contains **bromine**, the **M peak** and **M+2 peak** will both have the **same** height.

If you spot an **M+4 peak** it's because the molecule contains **two** atoms of the **halogen**.
(This changes the ratios of the M and M+2 peaks though.)

Mass Spectrometry

And Here's One More Example...

So, a mass spectrum can give you loads of information. Have a look at this one.
It's of an **oxygen-containing organic compound**:

Adding ^{35}Cl and ^{37}Cl in turn to the fragment of mass 43 (CH_3CO^+) gives the correct M_r values of **78** and **80**.
So the formula of the molecule is **CH_3COCl (ethanoyl chloride)**.

The masses of the fragments at 63 and 65 also differ by **2 units**. So they're likely to contain
the ^{35}Cl and ^{37}Cl isotopes. They're due to the fragments **$CO^{35}Cl^+$** and **$CO^{37}Cl^+$**.

Practice Questions

Q1 What is meant by the term 'molecular ion'?

Q2 Why do compounds containing chlorine or bromine have two molecular ion peaks?

Q3 Explain why the M+1 peak is formed and why it is always small.

Q4 What would be the mass of the fragment $CH_3CH_2CH_2^+$?

Exam Question

1   On the right is the mass spectrum of a haloalkane.
    Use the spectrum to answer the questions below.

a) Does the molecule contain chlorine or bromine? Explain how you know.   [2 marks]

b) What are the two main molecular masses of this haloalkane?   [1 mark]

c) Give the formulae of the fragments labelled A, B and C.   [3 marks]

d) Suggest a molecular formula for this molecule and draw its structure. Explain your suggestion.   [4 marks]

Unstable fragments — that's my brain on a Monday morning...

So mass spectrometry's a bit like weighing yourself, then taking bits off your body, weighing them separately, then trying to work out how they all fit together. Luckily you won't get anything as complicated as a body, and you won't need to cut yourself up either. Good news all round. Learn this page and watch out for the M+1 and M+2 peaks in the exam.

NMR Spectroscopy

NMR isn't the easiest of things, so ingest this information one piece at a time — a bit like eating a bar of chocolate (but this isn't so yummy).

NMR Gives You Information About a Molecule's Structure

There are two types of **nuclear magnetic resonance** (**NMR**) spectroscopy that you need to know about — ^{13}**C NMR**, which gives you information about how the **carbon atoms** in a molecule are arranged, and ^{1}**H** (or **proton**) **NMR**, which tells you how the **hydrogen atoms** in a molecule are arranged.

Any atomic nucleus with an **odd** number of nucleons (protons and neutrons) in its nucleus has a **nuclear spin**. This causes it to have a weak **magnetic field** — a bit like a bar magnet. NMR spectroscopy looks at how this tiny magnetic field reacts when you put in a much larger external magnetic field.

Hydrogen nuclei are **single protons**, so they have spin. **Carbon** usually has six protons and six neutrons, so it **doesn't** have spin. But about 1% of carbon atoms are the isotope ^{13}C (six protons and seven neutrons), which does have spin.

Nuclei Align in Two Directions in an External Magnetic Field

1) Normally the nuclei are spinning in **random directions** — so their magnetic fields **cancel out**.

2) But when a strong **external** magnetic field is applied, the nuclei will all align either **with the field** or **opposed to it**.

3) The nuclei aligned with the external field are at a **slightly lower energy level** than the opposed nuclei.

4) **Radio waves** of the right frequency can give the nuclei that are aligned with the external magnetic field enough energy to flip up to the higher energy level. The nuclei opposed to the external field, can **emit** radio waves and flip down to the lower energy level.

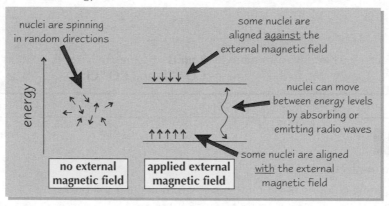

5) To start with, there are more nuclei **aligned** with the external field, so there will be an **overall absorption** of energy. NMR spectroscopy **measures** this **absorption**.

Nuclei in Different Environments Absorb Different Amounts of Energy

1) A nucleus is partly **shielded** from the effects of an external magnetic field by its **surrounding electrons**.

2) Any **other atoms** and **groups of atoms** that are around a nucleus will also affect the amount of electron shielding.
   E.g. If a carbon atom bonds to a more electronegative atom (like oxygen) the amount of electron shielding around its nucleus will decrease.

3) So the nuclei in a molecule feel different magnetic fields depending on their **environments**. This means that they absorb **different amounts** of energy at **different frequencies**.

Chemical Shift is Measured Relative to Tetramethylsilane

1) Nuclei in different environments absorb energy of **different frequencies**. NMR spectroscopy measures these differences relative to a **standard substance** — the difference is called the **chemical shift** (δ).

2) The standard substance is **tetramethylsilane** (**TMS**), $Si(CH_3)_4$. This molecule has 12 hydrogen atoms all in **identical environments**, so it produces a **single** absorption peak, well away from most other absorption peaks.

Tetramethylsilane is also inert (so it doesn't react with the sample), non-toxic, and volatile (so it's easy to remove from the sample).

3) Chemical shift is measured in **parts per million** (or **ppm**) relative to TMS. So the single peak produced by TMS is given a **chemical shift value of 0**.

4) You'll often see a peak at $\delta = 0$ on spectra because TMS is added to the test compound for calibration purposes.

NMR Spectroscopy

^{13}C NMR Tells You How Many Different Carbon Environments a Molecule Has

If you have a sample of a chemical that contains **carbon** atoms, you can use a ^{13}C NMR spectrum of the molecule to help work out what it is. The spectrum will have **one peak** on it for each **carbon environment** in the molecule.

There are **two carbon atoms** in a molecule of **ethanol**:

Because they are bonded to **different** atoms, each has a **different** amount of **electron shielding** — so there are **two carbon environments** in the ethanol molecule...

...and **two peaks** on its ^{13}C NMR spectrum.

^{13}C NMR spectra are usually much **simpler** than ^1H NMR spectra — they have fewer, sharper peaks. Here are some more examples:

ETHANE

Both carbon nuclei in ethane have the **same environment**. Each C has 3 Hs and a CH_3 group attached.

So ethane has one peak on its ^{13}C NMR spectrum.

^{13}C NMR spectrum of ethane

chemical shift, δ   0

PROPANONE

In propanone there are **two different carbon environments**. The **end carbons** both have the same environment — they each have 3 Hs and a $COCH_3$ attached. The **centre carbon** has 2 CH_3 groups and an O attached by a double bond.

So propanone's ^{13}C NMR spectrum has **2 peaks**.

^{13}C NMR spectrum of propanone

chemical shift, δ   0

CYCLOHEXANE-1,3-DIOL

In cyclohexane-1,3-diol there are **four different carbon environments**. If you think about the symmetry of the molecule you can see why this is. So cyclohexane-1,3-diol's ^{13}C NMR spectrum will have **4 peaks**.

Each different carbon environment is shown in a different colour.

Practice Questions

Q1 Which part of the electromagnetic spectrum is absorbed in NMR spectroscopy?

Q2 What is a chemical shift?

Q3 Explain what the number of peaks in a ^{13}C NMR shows.

Exam Questions

1 Draw the molecular structures of each of the following compounds and predict the number of peaks in the ^{13}C NMR spectrum of each compound.
   a) ethyl ethanoate   [2 marks]
   b) 1-chloro-2-methylpropane   [2 marks]
   c) 1,3,5-trichlorocyclohexane   [2 marks]

2 The molecule shown on the right is methoxyethane.
   It has the molecular formula C_3H_8O.
   a) Draw the displayed formulae of the two other possible isomers of C_3H_8O.   [2 marks]
   b) The ^{13}C NMR spectrum of one of the three isomers is on the right.
      Deduce which of the three isomers it represents. Explain your answer.   [2 marks]
   c) What is responsible for the peak at 0?   [1 mark]

NMR, TMS — IMO this page goes a bit OTT on the TLAs...

The ideas behind NMR are difficult, so don't worry if you have to read these pages quite a few times before they make sense. You've got to make sure you really understand the stuff on these two pages, cos there's more on the next two — and they aren't any easier. Keep bashing away at it though — you'll eventually go "aaah... I get it".

More About NMR

And now that you know the basics, here's the really crunchy bit for you to get your teeth stuck in.

¹H NMR — How Many **Environments** and How Many **Hydrogens** Are In Each

Each peak on a ¹H NMR spectrum is due to one or more hydrogen nuclei (protons) in a **particular environment** — this is similar to a ¹³C NMR spectrum (which tells you the number of different carbon environments).

But, with ¹H NMR, the **relative area** under each peak also tells you the **relative number** of H atoms in each environment.

¹H NMR spectrum of ethanoic acid, CH₃COOH

there are two peaks so there are H atoms in two different environments.

ratio of areas under peaks = 1:3

peak due to TMS — set at 0.

Absorption

Chemical shift, δ (ppm)

1) There are **two peaks** — so there are **two environments**.

2) The area ratio is **1:3** — so there's 1 H atom in the environment at δ = 11.5 ppm to every 3 H atoms in the other environment.

3) If you look at the structure of ethanoic acid, this makes sense:

3 H atoms attached to CH₂COOH.

1 H atom attached to COOCH₃.

¹H NMR is all about how **hydrogen nuclei** react to a magnetic field. The nucleus of a hydrogen atom is a **single proton**. So ¹H NMR is also known as '**proton NMR**' — and you might see the hydrogen atoms involved being called 'protons'.

Use a **Table** to Identify the **Hydrogen Atom** Causing the **Chemical Shift**

You use a table like this to **identify** which functional group each peak is due to.

Don't worry — **you don't need to learn it**. You'll be given one in your exam, so use it. The copy you get in your exam may look a little different, and have different values — they depend on the solvent, temperature and concentration.

According to the table, ethanoic acid (CH₃COOH) should have a peak at 11 – 11.7 ppm due to R-COO**H**, and a peak at 2.0 – 2.9 ppm due to R-COC**H₃**.

You can see these peaks on ethanoic acid's spectrum above.

Chemical shift, δ (ppm)	Type of H atom
0.8 – 1.3	R – CH₃
1.2 – 1.4	R – CH₂ – R
2.0 – 2.9	R – COCH₃
3.2 – 3.7	halogen – CH₃
3.6 – 3.8	R – CH₂ – Cl
3.3 – 3.9	R – OCH₂ – R
3.3 – 4.0	R – CH₂OH
3.5 – 5.5	R – OH
7.3	⌬ – OH
9.5 – 10	R – CHO
11.0 – 11.7	R – COOH

The hydrogen atoms that cause the shift are highlighted in red. R stands for any alkyl group.

Splitting Patterns Provide More Detail About Structure

The peaks may be **split** into smaller peaks. Peaks always split into the number of hydrogens on the neighbouring carbon, **plus one**. It's called the **n+1 rule**.

Type of Peak	Number of Hydrogens on Adjacent Carbon
Singlet (not split)	0
Doublet (split into two)	1
Triplet (split into three)	2
Quartet (split into four)	3

Here's the ¹H NMR spectrum for **1,1,2-trichloroethane**:

The peak due to the green hydrogens is split into **two** because there's **one hydrogen** on the adjacent carbon atom.

The peak due to the red hydrogen is split into **three** because there are **two hydrogens** on the adjacent carbon atom.

these numbers show the ratio of the areas under the peaks

this peak's due to the red H atom

this peak's due to the green H atoms

Absorption

Chemical shift, δ (ppm)

More About NMR

Put All the *Information Together* to *Predict the Structure*

EXAMPLE Using the spectrum below, and the table of chemical shift data on page 56, predict the structure of the compound.

1) The peak at δ = **2.5 ppm** is likely to be due to an **R–COCH₃** group, and the peak at δ = **9.5 ppm** is likely to be due to an **R–CHO** group.

2) From the areas, there's one proton in the peak at δ = **9.5 ppm**, for every three in the peak at δ = **2.5 ppm**. This fits nicely with the first bit — so far so good.

3) The quartet's got **three** neighbouring hydrogens, and the doublet's got **one** — so it's likely these two groups are next to each other.

Now you know the molecule has to contain $\overset{O}{\underset{H}{C}}$– and $–\overset{O}{\overset{||}{C}}–\overset{H}{\underset{H}{C}}–H$, all you have to do is fit them together:

Integration Traces Show Areas More Clearly

When the peaks are split, it's not as easy to see the ratio of the **areas**, so an **integration trace** is often shown. The height increases are proportional to the areas.

So the **integration ratio** for this spectrum is **1:2** — this means that there's 1 H atom in the first environment, and 2 H atoms in the second environment.

Samples are Dissolved in **Hydrogen-Free Solvents**

1) If a sample has to be dissolved, then a solvent is needed that doesn't contain any **¹H atoms** — because these would show up on the spectrum and confuse things.

2) **Deuterated solvents** are often used — their hydrogen atoms have been replaced by **deuterium** (D or ²H). Deuterium's an isotope of hydrogen that's got two nucleons (a proton and a neutron).

3) Because deuterium has an **even number** of nucleons, it doesn't have a spin (so it doesn't create a magnetic field).

4) CCl₄ can also be used — it doesn't contain any ¹H atoms either.

Practice Questions

Q1 What causes peaks to split in proton NMR?

Q2 What causes a triplet of peaks?

Exam Questions

1 The ¹H NMR spectrum on the right is that of an haloalkane. Use the table of chemical shifts on page 56 to do the following:

  a) Predict the environment of the two H atoms with a shift of 3.6 ppm. [1 mark]

  b) Predict the environment of the three H atoms with a shift of 1.3 ppm. [1 mark]

  c) The molecular mass of the molecule is 64.5.
     Suggest a possible structure and explain your suggestion. [2 marks]

  d) Explain the shapes of the two peaks. [4 marks]

2 For the ¹H NMR spectrum of ethyl ethanoate, CH₃COOC₂H₅, give:

  a) the number of different hydrogen environments. [1 mark]

  b) the integration ratio (from left to right along the molecule, as given above). [1 mark]

  c) the types of peaks you will see (in the same order as the integration ratio). [1 mark]

Never mind splitting peaks — this stuff's likely to cause splitting headaches...

Is your head spinning yet? I know mine is. Round and round like a merry-go-round. It's a hard life when you're tied to a desk trying to get NMR spectroscopy firmly fixed in your head. You must be looking quite peaky by now... so go on, learn this stuff, take the dog around the block, then come back and see if you can still remember it all.

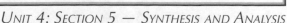

IR Spectroscopy and Chromatography

Chromatography's all about separating mixtures of chemicals — like the old 'felt tip on filter paper' experiment. You need to know about a few different types of chromatography at A2. There's a bit of revision on infrared spectroscopy to do first too...

Infrared Spectroscopy Helps You Identify Organic Molecules

1) In infrared (IR) spectroscopy, a beam of **IR radiation** goes through the sample.
2) The IR energy is absorbed by the **bonds** in the molecules, increasing their **vibrational** energy.
3) **Different bonds** absorb **different wavelengths**. Bonds in different **environments** in a molecule absorb different wavelengths too — so the O–H group in an **alcohol** and the O–H in a **carboxylic acid** absorb different wavelengths.
4) This table shows what **frequencies** different groups absorb —

Functional group	Where it's found	Frequency/ Wavenumber (cm⁻¹)	Type of absorption
C–H	most organic molecules	2800 – 3100	strong, sharp
O–H	alcohols	3200 – 3750	strong, broad
O–H	carboxylic acids	2500 – 3300	medium, very broad
C–O	alcohols, carboxylic acids and esters	1100 – 1310	strong, sharp
C=O	aldehydes, ketones, carboxylic acids and esters	1680 – 1800	strong, sharp
C=O	amides	1630 – 1700	medium
C=C	alkenes	1620 – 1680	medium, sharp
N–H	primary amines	3300 – 3500	medium to strong
N–H	amides	about 3500	medium

> This tells you what the trough on the graph will look like.

> O–H groups tend to have broad absorptions — it's because they take part in hydrogen bonding.

Clark began to regret having an infrared mechanism installed in his glasses.

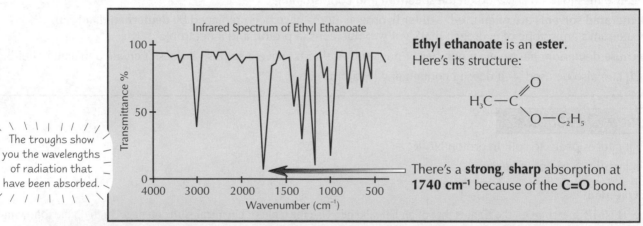

Infrared Spectrum of Ethyl Ethanoate

> The troughs show you the wavelengths of radiation that have been absorbed.

Ethyl ethanoate is an **ester**. Here's its structure:

There's a **strong, sharp** absorption at **1740 cm⁻¹** because of the **C=O** bond.

Infrared Spectrum of Propenamide

Here's the structure of **propenamide**:

Medium absorption due to the **N-H (amide)** bond.

Medium absorption due to the **C=O** bond.

Medium, sharp absorption due to the **C=C** bond.

IR Spectroscopy and Chromatography

Chromatography is Good for **Separating** and **Identifying** Things

Chromatography is used to **separate** stuff in a mixture — once it's separated out, you can often **identify** the components.

There are quite a few different types of chromatography — but the ones you need to know about are **column chromatography** and **gas-liquid chromatography** (GLC). All types of chromatography have two phases:

> 1) A **mobile phase** — where the molecules can move. This is always a liquid or a gas.
> 2) A **stationary phase** — where the molecules can't move. This must be a solid, or a liquid held in a solid.

The components in the mixture **separate out** as the mobile phase moves through the stationary phase.

Column Chromatography is Used To Separate Out **Solutions**

Column chromatography is mostly used for **purifying an organic product.** ◄ *This needs to be done to separate it from unreacted chemicals or side products.*

1) It involves packing a glass column with a slurry of an absorbent material such as aluminium oxide, coated with water. This is the **stationary phase**.

2) The mixture to be separated is added to the top of the column and allowed to drain down into the slurry. A **solvent** is then run slowly and continually through the column. This solvent is the **mobile phase**.

3) As the mixture is washed through the column, its components **separate out** according to **how soluble** they are in the mobile phase and **how strongly they are adsorbed** onto the stationary phase (**retention).**

4) Each different component will spend some time adsorbed onto the stationary phase and some time dissolved in the mobile phase. The **more** soluble each component is in the mobile phase, the **quicker** it'll pass through the column.

Stationary phase (water-coated particles of Al_2O_3)

SOLVENT

As the solvent passes through, some components are strongly adsorbed onto the Al_2O_3.

Other components are less strongly adsorbed and are more soluble in the solvent. These pass through the column more quickly.

Gas-Liquid Chromatography is Used To Separate **Mixtures of Volatile Liquids**

1) If you've got a mixture of **volatile liquids** (ones that turn into gases easily), then **gas-liquid chromatography** (GLC) is the way to separate them out so that you can **identify** them.

2) The stationary phase is a **viscous liquid**, such as an oil, which coats the inside of a long tube, which is coiled to save space, and built into an oven. The mobile phase is an **unreactive carrier gas** such as nitrogen.

3) Each component takes a different amount of time from being **injected** into the tube to being **recorded** at the other end. This is the **retention time**.

The retention time depends on how much time the component spends moving along with the carrier gas, and how much time it spends stuck to the viscous liquid.

sample's injected here

carrier gas enters here

temperature-controlled oven

detector and recorder

G.L.C. chromatogram
retention time

Recorder response

Time/min

4) Each separate substance will have a unique retention time — so you can use the retention time to **identify** the components of the mixture. (You have to run a known sample under the same conditions for comparison). For example, if you wanted to know if a mixture contained **octane**, you could run a sample of the **mixture** through the system, then run a sample of **pure octane** through, and see if there's a peak at the **same retention time** on both spectra.

5) The **area** under each peak tells you the relative **amount** of each component that's present in the mixture.

6) GLC can be used to find the **level of alcohol** in **blood** or **urine** — the results are **accurate** enough to be used as evidence in court. It's also used to find the **proportions** of various **esters in oils** used in **paints** — this lets picture restorers know exactly what paint was originally used.

IR Spectroscopy and Chromatography

And now you get this whole page of questions on chromatography and IR Spectra. Keep at it until they're all a doddle.

Practice Questions

Q1 Alcohols and carboxylic acids both contain an OH functional group. Suggest how you could tell the difference between the infrared spectrum of an alcohol and the infrared spectrum of a carboxylic acid.

Q2 What are the two phases in chromatography?

Q3 In column chromatography, explain why the components pass through the column at different rates.

Q4 Give an example of a gas that is used as a carrier gas in gas-liquid chromatography.

Q5 GLC can identify which substances are present and their relative amounts. How is the relative amount determined?

Exam Questions

1   GLC can be used to detect the presence and quantity of alcohol in the blood or urine samples of suspected drink-drivers.

   a) What do the letters GLC stand for?   [1 mark]

   b) Explain how 'retention time' is used to identify ethanol in a sample of blood or urine.   [2 marks]

   c) Why is nitrogen used as the carrier gas?   [1 mark]

2   A molecule with a molecular mass of 74 gives the following IR spectrum.

   Use the data table on p58 to help you answer the following questions.

   a) Which functional groups produce the troughs labelled A – D?   [4 marks]

   b) Suggest a molecular formula and name for this molecule. Explain your suggestion.   [3 marks]

3   A student makes an unbranched ester with the molecular formula $C_4H_8O_2$ by refluxing a carboxylic acid with ethanol. The student records an IR spectrum of the reaction mixture before and after refluxing.

   Use the data table on p58 to help you answer the following questions.

   a) Give the structural formula of

   (i)   the unbranched ester made.   [1 mark]

   (ii)   the carboxylic acid that was reacted with ethanol.   [1 mark]

   b) The IR that was recorded **before** refluxing had a strong peak at 1719 cm⁻¹.
      Which substance caused this peak? Explain your answer.   [3 marks]

   c) Describe the features of the IR spectrum of the unbranched ester that would be

   (i)   different from that of the reaction mixture.   [3 marks]

   (ii)   similar to that of the reaction mixture.   [4 marks]

            Explain what causes each of the features that you refer to.

Ooooh — I'm picking up some good vibrations...

Now, I've warned you — infrared glasses are not for fun. They're highly advanced pieces of technology which if placed in the wrong hands could cause havoc and destruction across the Universe. Luckily, you'll be given a data table for IR spectra in the exam, so you don't have to bother learning it. But DO learn how the different types of chromatography work.

Lattice Enthalpies

I'm sure you all remember enthalpies from AS... but here's a quick reminder just in case...

First — *A Few Definitions* You Should Remember

ΔH is the symbol for **enthalpy change**. Enthalpy change is the **heat** energy transferred in a reaction at **constant pressure**.

$\Delta H^{\ominus}$ means that the enthalpy change was measured under **standard conditions** (**100 kPa and 298 K**).
Exothermic reactions have a **negative ΔH** value, because heat energy is given out.
Endothermic reactions have a **positive ΔH** value, because heat energy is absorbed.

Lattice Enthalpy is a Measure of *Ionic Bond Strength*

Lattice enthalpy can be defined in two ways:

> ① **Lattice formation enthalpy**: the enthalpy change when **1 mole** of a **solid ionic compound** is **formed** from its **gaseous ions** under standard conditions.
>
> **Example:**
> $Na^{+}_{(g)} + Cl^{-}_{(g)} \rightarrow NaCl_{(s)}$ $\quad \Delta H^{\ominus} = -787$ kJ mol^{-1} (exothermic)
> $Mg^{2+}_{(g)} + 2Cl^{-}_{(g)} \rightarrow MgCl_{2(s)}$ $\quad \Delta H^{\ominus} = -2526$ kJ mol^{-1} (exothermic)

> ② **Lattice dissociation enthalpy**: the enthalpy change when **1 mole** of a **solid ionic compound** is completely **dissociated** into its **gaseous ions** under standard conditions.
>
> **Example:**
> $NaCl_{(s)} \rightarrow Na^{+}_{(g)} + Cl^{-}_{(g)}$ $\quad \Delta H^{\ominus} = +787$ kJ mol^{-1} (endothermic)
> $MgCl_{2(s)} \rightarrow Mg^{2+}_{(g)} + 2Cl^{-}_{(g)}$ $\quad \Delta H^{\ominus} = +2526$ kJ mol^{-1} (endothermic)

You can calculate the lattice enthalpy of formation using the method on page 65.

Part of the sodium chloride lattice

Notice that lattice formation enthalpy and lattice dissociation enthalpy are exact opposites.

You *Can't* Measure Lattice Enthalpy **Directly**

Lattice enthalpy **can't** be measured directly, but it **can** be calculated with a **Born-Haber cycle** — all will be revealed on the next page. But first you need to know these **definitions**:

> **Enthalpy change of formation, ΔH_{f},** is the enthalpy change when **1 mole** of a **compound** is formed from its **elements** in their standard states under standard conditions, e.g. $2C_{(s)} + 3H_{2(g)} + \frac{1}{2}O_{2(g)} \rightarrow C_2H_5OH_{(l)}$

> The **bond dissociation enthalpy, ΔH_{diss},** is the enthalpy change when all the **bonds of the same type** in **1 mole** of **gaseous molecules** are broken, e.g. $Cl_{2(g)} \rightarrow 2Cl_{(g)}$

> **Enthalpy change of atomisation of an element, ΔH_{at},** is the enthalpy change when **1 mole** of **gaseous atoms** is formed from an element in its **standard state**, e.g. $\frac{1}{2}Cl_{2(g)} \rightarrow Cl_{(g)}$

> **Enthalpy change of atomisation of a compound, ΔH_{at},** is the enthalpy change when **1 mole** of a compound in its **standard state** is converted to **gaseous atoms**, e.g. $NaCl_{(s)} \rightarrow Na_{(g)} + Cl_{(g)}$

> The **first ionisation enthalpy, ΔH_{ie1},** is the enthalpy change when **1 mole** of **gaseous 1+ ions** is formed from **1 mole** of **gaseous atoms**, e.g. $Mg_{(g)} \rightarrow Mg^{+}_{(g)} + e^{-}$

> The **second ionisation enthalpy, ΔH_{ie2},** is the enthalpy change when **1 mole** of **gaseous 2+ ions** is formed from **1 mole** of **gaseous 1+ ions**, e.g. $Mg^{+}_{(g)} \rightarrow Mg^{2+}_{(g)} + e^{-}$

> **First electron affinity, ΔH_{ea1},** is the enthalpy change when **1 mole** of gaseous **1– ions** is made from **1 mole** of gaseous **atoms**, e.g. $O_{(g)} + e^{-} \rightarrow O^{-}_{(g)}$

> **Second electron affinity, ΔH_{ea2},** is the enthalpy change when **1 mole** of gaseous **2– ions** is made from **1 mole** of gaseous **1– ions**, e.g. $O^{-}_{(g)} + e^{-} \rightarrow O^{2-}_{(g)}$

> The **enthalpy change of hydration, ΔH_{hyd},** is the enthalpy change when **1 mole** of **aqueous ions** is formed from **gaseous ions**, e.g. $Na^{+}_{(g)} \rightarrow Na^{+}_{(aq)}$

> The **enthalpy change of solution, $\Delta H_{solution}$,** is the enthalpy change when **1 mole** of **solute** is dissolved in **sufficient solvent** that no further enthalpy change occurs on further dilution, e.g. $NaCl_{(s)} \rightarrow NaCl_{(aq)}$

Lattice Enthalpies

Now you know all your enthalpy change definitions, here's how to use them... Enjoy.

Born-Haber Cycles can be Used to Calculate Lattice Enthalpies

You can't calculate a lattice enthalpy **directly**, so you have to use a **Born-Haber cycle** to figure out what the enthalpy change would be if you took **another, less direct, route**. **Hess's law** says that the **total enthalpy change** of a reaction is always the **same**, no matter which route is taken.

Here's how to draw a Born-Haber cycle for calculating the lattice enthalpy of **NaCl**:

2 Then put the enthalpies of atomisation and ionisation above this.

1 Start with the enthalpy of formation here.

First ionisation enthalpy of sodium (+496 kJmol⁻¹)

Atomisation enthalpy of sodium (+107 kJmol⁻¹)

Atomisation enthalpy of chlorine (+122 kJmol⁻¹)

Enthalpy of formation of sodium chloride (−411 kJmol⁻¹)

$Na^+_{(g)} + e^- + Cl_{(g)}$

$\Delta H4$

$Na_{(g)} + Cl_{(g)}$ (gaseous atoms)

$\Delta H3$

$Na_{(s)} + Cl_{(g)}$

$\Delta H2$

$Na_{(s)} + \frac{1}{2}Cl_{2(g)}$ (standard states)

$\Delta H1$

$NaCl_{(s)}$ (ionic lattice)

3 The electron affinity goes up here...

First electron affinity of chlorine (−349 kJmol⁻¹)

$\Delta H5$

$Na^+_{(g)} + Cl^-_{(g)}$

$\Delta H6$ Lattice enthalpy of formation of sodium chloride

4 ...and lattice enthalpy goes down here.

There are **two routes** you can follow to get from the elements in their **standard states** to the **ionic lattice**. The green arrow shows the **direct route** and the purple arrows show the **indirect route**. The enthalpy change for each is the **same**.

From Hess's law: $\Delta H6 = -\Delta H5 - \Delta H4 - \Delta H3 - \Delta H2 + \Delta H1$
$= -(-349) - (+496) - (+107) - (+122) + (-411) = -787 \text{ kJmol}^{-1}$

So the **lattice enthalpy of formation** of sodium chloride is **−787 kJmol⁻¹**.

You need a minus sign if you go the wrong way along an arrow.

Calculations Involving Group 2 Elements are a Bit Different

Born-Haber cycles for compounds containing **Group 2 elements** have a few **changes** from the one above. Make sure you understand what's going on so you can handle whatever compound they throw at you.

Here's the Born-Haber cycle for calculating the lattice enthalpy of **magnesium chloride** ($MgCl_2$).

1 Group 2 elements form 2+ ions — so you've got to include the second ionisation enthalpy.

Second ionisation enthalpy of magnesium

First ionisation enthalpy of magnesium

Atomisation enthalpy of magnesium

Atomisation enthalpy of chlorine ×2

2 There's 2 moles of chlorine ions in each mole of $MgCl_2$ — so you need to double the atomisation enthalpy of chlorine...

Enthalpy of formation of magnesium chloride

$Mg^{2+}_{(g)} + 2e^- + 2Cl_{(g)}$

$Mg^+_{(g)} + e^- + 2Cl_{(g)}$

$Mg_{(g)} + 2Cl_{(g)}$

$Mg_{(s)} + 2Cl_{(g)}$

$Mg_{(s)} + Cl_{2(g)}$

$MgCl_{2(s)}$

$Mg^{2+}_{(g)} + 2Cl^-_{(g)}$

First electron affinity of chlorine ×2

3 ...and you need to double the first electron affinity of chlorine too (because you're forming 2 moles of Cl^- ions).

Lattice enthalpy of formation of magnesium chloride

Theoretical Lattice Enthalpies are Often Different from Experimental Values

You can work out a **theoretical lattice enthalpy** by doing some calculations based on the **purely ionic model** of a lattice. The purely ionic model of a lattice assumes that all the ions are **spherical**, and have their charge **evenly distributed** around them.

But the **experimental lattice enthalpy** from the Born-Haber cycle is usually different. This is **evidence** that ionic compounds usually have some **covalent character**.

The positive and negative ions in a lattice **aren't** usually exactly spherical Positive ions **polarise** neighbouring negative ions to different extents, and the **more polarisation** there is, the **more covalent** the bonding will be.

 unpolarised ions — purely ionic bonding

 polarised ions — partial covalent bonding

Lattice Enthalpies

Comparing Lattice Enthalpies Can Tell You 'How Ionic' an Ionic Lattice Is

If the experimental and theoretical lattice enthalpies for a compound are **very different**, it shows that the compound has a lot of covalent character.

For example, here are both lattice enthalpy values for some **magnesium halides**.

Compound	Lattice Enthalpy of Formation (kJmol⁻¹)	
	From experimental values in Born-Haber cycle	From theory
Magnesium chloride	−2526	−2326
Magnesium bromide	−2440	−2097
Magnesium iodide	−2327	−1944

1) The **experimental** lattice energies are **bigger** than the theoretical values by a fair bit.
2) This tells you that the **bonding** is **stronger** than the calculations from the ionic model predict.
3) The difference shows that the ionic bonds in the magnesium halides are quite strongly **polarised** and so they have **quite a lot of covalent character**.

Here are some more lattice energies, for **sodium halides** this time:

1) The experimental and theoretical values are a **pretty close match** — so you can say that these compounds fit the 'purely ionic' model very well.
2) This indicates that the structure of the lattice for these compounds is quite close to being **purely ionic**. There's almost no polarisation so they don't have much covalent character.

Compound	Lattice Enthalpy of Formation (kJmol⁻¹)	
	From experimental values in Born-Haber cycle	From theory
Sodium chloride	−787	−766
Sodium bromide	−742	−731
Sodium iodide	−698	−686

Practice Questions

Q1 Define *first ionisation enthalpy* and *first electron affinity*.

Q2 Sketch out Born-Haber cycles for: a) LiF, b) CaCl$_2$.

Q3 Explain why theoretical lattice enthalpies are often different from experimentally determined lattice enthalpies.

Exam Questions

1 Using the data below:
   a) Construct a Born-Haber cycle for potassium bromide (KBr).   [4 marks]
   b) Use your Born-Haber cycle to calculate the lattice enthalpy of formation of potassium bromide.   [3 marks]

$\Delta H_f^{\ominus}$ [potassium bromide] = −394 kJmol⁻¹ $\Delta H_{at}^{\ominus}$ [bromine] = +112 kJmol⁻¹ $\Delta H_{at}^{\ominus}$ [potassium] = +89 kJmol⁻¹

$\Delta H_{ie1}^{\ominus}$ [potassium] = +419 kJmol⁻¹ $\Delta H_{ea1}^{\ominus}$ [bromine] = −325 kJmol⁻¹

2 The diagram shows part of a Born-Haber cycle for copper(II) chloride.
   a) Identify the enthalpy changes X, Y and Z.   [3 marks]
   b) What other enthalpy changes need to be added in order to complete the cycle?   [3 marks]

Using Born-Haber cycles — it's just like riding a bike...

All this energy going in and out can get a bit confusing. Remember these simple rules: 1) It takes energy to break bonds, but energy is given out when bonds are made. 2) A negative ΔH means energy is given out (it's exothermic). 3) A positive ΔH means energy is taken in (it's endothermic). 4) Never return to a firework once lit.

Enthalpies of Solution

Once you know what's happening when you stir sugar into your tea, your cuppa'll be twice as enjoyable.

Dissolving Involves Enthalpy Changes

When a solid **ionic lattice** dissolves in water these **two** things happen:

1) The bonds between the ions **break** — this is **endothermic**.
   This enthalpy change is the **lattice enthalpy of dissociation**.

2) Bonds between the ions and the water are **made** — this is **exothermic**.
   The enthalpy change here is called the **enthalpy change of hydration**.

Ionic lattice.

ions in a lattice   separate ions   hydrated ions

Oxygen is more electronegative than hydrogen, so it draws the bonding electrons toward itself, creating a dipole.

3) The **enthalpy change of solution** is the overall effect on the enthalpy of these two things.

Enthalpy Change of Solution can be Calculated

You can work out the enthalpy change of solution using an **enthalpy cycle**.
You just need to know the **lattice dissociation enthalpy** of the compound and the enthalpies of **hydration of the ions**.

Here's how to draw the enthalpy cycle for working out the **enthalpy change of solution** for **sodium chloride**.

1 Put the ionic lattice and the dissolved ions on the top — connect them by the enthalpy change of solution. This is the direct route.

2 Connect the ionic lattice to the gaseous ions by the lattice enthalpy of dissociation. This will be a positive number.

Lattice dissociation enthalpy (+787 kJmol⁻¹)

If you're given a negative value for lattice enthalpy, it'll be the lattice enthalpy of formation. It's the reverse of this that you want (see page 61)

$$NaCl_{(s)} \xrightarrow[\Delta H3]{\text{Enthalpy change of solution}} Na^+_{(aq)} + Cl^-_{(aq)}$$

$\Delta H1$ $\Delta H2$

Enthalpy of hydration of $Na^+_{(g)}$ (−406 kJmol⁻¹)
Enthalpy of hydration of $Cl^-_{(g)}$ (−364 kJmol⁻¹)

$$Na^+_{(g)} + Cl^-_{(g)}$$

3 Connect the gaseous ions to the dissolved ions by the hydration enthalpies of **each** ion. This completes the indirect route.

From Hess's law: $\Delta H3 = \Delta H1 + \Delta H2 = +787 + (−406 + −364) =$ **+17 kJmol⁻¹**

The enthalpy change of solution is **slightly endothermic**, but this is compensated for by a small increase in **entropy** (see page 66), so sodium chloride still dissolves in water.

And here's another. This one's for working out the **enthalpy change of solution** for **silver chloride**.

$$AgCl_{(s)} \xrightarrow[\Delta H3]{\text{Enthalpy change of solution}} Ag^+_{(aq)} + Cl^-_{(aq)}$$

$\Delta H1$ $\Delta H2$

Lattice dissociation enthalpy (+905 kJmol⁻¹)

Enthalpy of hydration of $Ag^+_{(g)}$ (−464 kJmol⁻¹)
Enthalpy of hydration of $Cl^-_{(g)}$ (−364 kJmol⁻¹)

$$Ag^+_{(g)} + Cl^-_{(g)}$$

From Hess's law: $\Delta H3 = \Delta H1 + \Delta H2 = +905 + (−464 + −364) =$ **+77 kJmol⁻¹**

This is much **more endothermic** than the enthalpy change of solution for sodium chloride. There is an **increase in entropy** again, but it's pretty small and not enough to make a difference — so silver chloride is **insoluble** in water.

Enthalpies of Solution

Use **Mean Bond Enthalpies** to Calculate Enthalpy Changes

Energy is **taken in** when bonds are **broken** and **released** when bonds are **formed**, so —

> enthalpy change for a reaction = sum of enthalpies of bonds broken – sum of enthalpies of bonds formed

If you need **more** energy to **break** bonds than is released when bonds are made, it's an **endothermic reaction** and the enthalpy change, ΔH, is **positive**. If **more** energy is **released** than is taken in, it's **exothermic** and ΔH is **negative**.

Example: Calculate the enthalpy change for the following reaction: $N_{2(g)} + 3H_{2(g)} \rightarrow 2NH_{3(g)}$

Bond	Mean bond enthalpy (kJmol⁻¹)
N≡N	945
H—H	436
N—H	391

It's easier to see what's going on if you **sketch out** the molecules involved:

$$N\equiv N \ + \ 3H-H \longrightarrow 2\ H-\underset{\overset{|}{H}}{N}-H$$

Now add up the mean bond enthalpies for the reactant **bonds broken**...

$(1 \times N\equiv N) + (3 \times H-H) = (1 \times 945) + (3 \times 436) = 2253$ kJmol⁻¹

...and for the **new bonds formed** in the products

$(6 \times N-H) = (6 \times 391) = 2346$ kJmol⁻¹

So the **enthalpy change for the reaction** $= 2253 - 2346 = $ **–93 kJmol⁻¹**.

You can use this method to calculate the lattice enthalpy of formation — see page 61.

It's negative, so it's exothermic.

Mean Bond Enthalpy Calculations are Only **Approximations**

The bond enthalpy given above for N–H bonds is **not** exactly right for **every** N–H bond. A given type of bond will **vary in strength** from compound to compound and can even vary **within** a compound. Mean bond enthalpies are the **averages** of these bond enthalpies. Only the bond enthalpies of **diatomic molecules**, such as H_2 and HCl, will always be the same.

So calculations done using **mean bond enthalpies** will never be perfectly accurate. You get much **more exact** results from **experimental data** obtained from the **specific compounds**.

Practice Questions

Q1 Describe the two things that happen when something dissolves.

Q2 Without peeking, draw the enthalpy cycle that you'd use to work out the enthalpy change of solution of NaCl.

Q3 How can mean bond enthalpies be used to calculate enthalpy changes for covalent compounds?

Exam Questions

1 a) Draw an enthalpy cycle for the enthalpy change of solution of $SrF_{2(s)}$. Label each enthalpy change. [5 marks]

   b) Calculate the enthalpy change of solution for SrF_2 from the following data:

   $\Delta H^{\ominus}_{\text{latt}} [SrF_{2(s)}] = -2492$ kJmol⁻¹, $\Delta H^{\ominus}_{\text{hyd}} [Sr^{2+}_{(g)}] = -1480$ kJmol⁻¹, $\Delta H^{\ominus}_{\text{hyd}} [F^{-}_{(g)}] = -506$ kJmol⁻¹ [2 marks]

2 Show that the enthalpy change of solution for $MgCl_{2(s)}$ is –122 kJmol⁻¹, given that:

   $\Delta H^{\ominus}_{\text{latt}} [MgCl_{2(s)}] = -2526$ kJmol⁻¹, $\Delta H^{\ominus}_{\text{hyd}} [Mg^{2+}_{(g)}] = -1920$ kJmol⁻¹, $\Delta H^{\ominus}_{\text{hyd}} [Cl^{-}_{(g)}] = -364$ kJmol⁻¹. [3 marks]

3 a) Calculate the enthalpy change for $CH_{4(g)} + 2O_{2(g)} \rightarrow CO_{2(g)} + 2H_2O_{(g)}$ using the bond enthalpies in the table below.

Bond	C–H	O=O	C=O	O–H
Mean bond enthalpy (kJmol⁻¹)	412	496	743	463

[3 marks]

   b) Give a reason why the enthalpy change calculated by this method is not likely to be as accurate as one calculated using an enthalpy cycle. [2 marks]

Enthalpy change of solution of the Wicked Witch of the West = 8745 kJmol⁻¹ ...

Compared to the ones on page 62, these enthalpy cycles are an absolute breeze. You've got to make sure the definitions are firmly fixed in your mind though. And don't forget there are two opposite definitions of lattice enthalpy.

Entropy Change

Entropy sounds a bit like enthalpy (to start with at least), but they're not the same thing at all. Read on...

Entropy Tells You How Much Disorder There Is

Entropy is a measure of the **number of ways** that **particles** can be **arranged** and the **number of ways** that the **energy** can be shared out between the particles.

Substances really **like** disorder, so the particles move to try to **increase the entropy**.

There are a few things that affect entropy:

Entropy is represented by the symbol S

PHYSICAL STATE affects Entropy

You have to go back to the good old **solid-liquid-gas** particle explanation thingy to understand this.

Solid particles just wobble about a fixed point — there's **hardly any** randomness, so they have the **lowest entropy**.

Gas particles whizz around wherever they like. They've got the most **random arrangements** of particles, so they have the **highest entropy**.

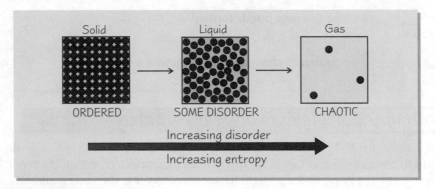

DISSOLVING affects Entropy

Dissolving a solid also increases its entropy — dissolved particles can **move freely** as they're no longer held in one place.

MORE PARTICLES means More Entropy

It makes sense — the more particles you've got, the **more ways** they and their energy can be **arranged**. — so in a reaction like $N_2O_{4(g)} \rightarrow 2NO_{2(g)}$, entropy increases because the **number of moles** increases.

Entropy Increase May Explain Spontaneous Endothermic Reactions

A **spontaneous** (or **feasible**) change is one that'll **just happen** by itself — you don't need to give it energy.

You might think that only exothermic reactions could be spontaneous because you need to supply energy to endothermic reactions. But the weird thing is, some **endothermic** reactions are **spontaneous**.

You normally do have to supply **energy** to make an endothermic reaction happen, but in some reactions the **entropy** increases such a lot that the reaction will happen **by itself**, without you supplying any energy.

For example,

- Water evaporates at room temperature. This change needs **energy** to break the bonds between the molecules (i.e. it's endothermic) — but because it's **changing state** (from a liquid to a gas), the **entropy increases**.

- The reaction of sodium hydrogencarbonate with hydrochloric acid is a **spontaneous endothermic reaction**. Again there's an **increase in entropy**.

$$NaHCO_{3(s)} \;+\; H^+_{(aq)} \;\rightarrow\; Na^+_{(aq)} \;+\; CO_{2(g)} \;+\; H_2O_{(l)}$$

1 mole solid   1 mole   1 mole   1 mole gas   1 mole liquid
         aqueous ions   aqueous ions

The product has more particles — and gases and liquids have more entropy than solids too.

Entropy Change

Reactions **Won't** Happen Unless the **Total Entropy Change** is **Positive**

During a reaction, there's an entropy change (ΔS) between the **reactants and products** — the entropy change of the **system**. The entropy of the **surroundings** changes too (because **energy** is transferred to or from the system). The **TOTAL entropy change** is the sum of the entropy changes of the **system** and the **surroundings**.

The units of entropy are JK⁻¹mol⁻¹

$$\Delta S_{total} = \Delta S_{system} + \Delta S_{surroundings}$$

This equation isn't much use unless you know ΔS_{system} and $\Delta S_{surroundings}$. Luckily, there are formulas for them too:

This is just the difference between the entropies of the reactants and products. →

$$\Delta S_{system} = S_{products} - S_{reactants}$$

and

$$\Delta S_{surroundings} = -\frac{\Delta H}{T}$$

← ΔH = enthalpy change (in Jmol⁻¹)
T = temperature (in K)

Here's an **Example** of How to **Calculate** the **Total Entropy Change**

Example: Calculate the total entropy change for the reaction of ammonia and hydrogen chloride under standard conditions.

$$NH_{3(g)} + HCl_{(g)} \rightarrow NH_4Cl_{(s)} \qquad \Delta H^{\ominus} = -315 \text{ kJmol}^{-1} \text{ (at 298 K)}$$

$$S^{\ominus}[NH_{3(g)}] = 192.3 \text{ JK}^{-1}\text{mol}^{-1}, \ S^{\ominus}[HCl_{(g)}] = 186.8 \text{ JK}^{-1}\text{mol}^{-1}, \ S^{\ominus}[NH_4Cl_{(s)}] = 94.6 \text{ JK}^{-1}\text{mol}^{-1}$$

First find the entropy change of the **system**:

$$\Delta S^{\ominus}_{system} = S^{\ominus}_{products} - S^{\ominus}_{reactants} = 94.6 - (192.3 + 186.8) = \textbf{-284.5 JK}^{-1}\textbf{mol}^{-1}$$

← This shows a negative change in entropy. It's not surprising, as 2 moles of gas have combined to form 1 mole of solid.

Now find the entropy change of the **surroundings**:

$$\Delta H^{\ominus} = -315 \text{ kJmol}^{-1} = -315 \times 10^3 \text{ Jmol}^{-1}$$ ← *Put $\Delta H^{\ominus}$ in the right units.*

$$\Delta S_{surroundings} = -\frac{\Delta H}{T} = \frac{-(-315 \times 10^3)}{298} = \textbf{+1057.0 JK}^{-1}\textbf{mol}^{-1}$$

Finally you can find the **total** entropy change:

$$\Delta S^{\ominus}_{total} = \Delta S^{\ominus}_{system} + \Delta S^{\ominus}_{surroundings} = -284.5 + (+1057.0) = \textbf{+772.5 JK}^{-1}\textbf{mol}^{-1}$$

*The total entropy has **increased**. The entropy increase in the surroundings was big enough to make up for the entropy decrease in the system.*

Practice Questions

Q1 What does the term 'entropy' mean?

Q2 In each of the following pairs choose the one with the greater entropy value.
   a) 1 mole of $NaCl_{(aq)}$ and 1 mole of $NaCl_{(s)}$ b) 1 mole of $Br_{2(l)}$ and 1 mole of $Br_{2(g)}$
   c) 1 mole of $Br_{2(g)}$ and 2 moles of $Br_{2(g)}$

Q3 Write down the formulas for the following:
   a) total entropy change   b) entropy change of the surroundings   c) entropy change of the system

Exam Question

1   The equation for the formation of magnesium oxide from magnesium and oxygen is shown below.

$$Mg_{(s)} + \tfrac{1}{2}O_{2(g)} \rightarrow MgO_{(s)}$$

   a)   Based on just the equation, predict whether the reaction is likely to be spontaneous. Give a reason for your answer.   [2 marks]

   b)   Use the data on the right to calculate the entropy change for the system above.   [3 marks]

Substance	Entropy — standard conditions (JK⁻¹mol⁻¹)
$Mg_{(s)}$	32.7
$\tfrac{1}{2}O_{2(g)}$	102.5
$MgO_{(s)}$	26.9

Being neat and tidy is against the laws of nature...

I know there are three different formulas on this page, but at least they aren't too hard to use. Watch out for your units, though — make sure the temperature's in kelvin. If you're given a temperature in °C, you need to subtract 273 from it to get it in kelvin. And check that all your enthalpy and entropy values involve joules, not kilojoules (so Jmol⁻¹, not kJmol⁻¹, etc.).

Free-Energy Change

Free energy — I could do with a bit of that. My gas bill is astronomical.

For Spontaneous Reactions ΔG must be Negative or Zero

Free energy change, ΔG, is a measure used to predict whether a reaction is **feasible**.

If ΔG is **negative or equal to zero**, then the reaction might happen by itself.

Free energy change takes into account the changes in **enthalpy** and **entropy** in the system. And of course, there's a formula for it:

ΔG = free energy change (in Jmol^{-1})

$$\Delta G = \Delta H - T\Delta S_{system}$$

ΔH = enthalpy change (in Jmol^{-1})
T = temperature (in K)
ΔS_{system} = entropy of the system (in JK^{-1}mol^{-1}) (see page 67)

Even if ΔG shows that a reaction is theoretically feasible, it might have a really high activation energy and be so slow that you wouldn't notice it happening at all.

Example: Calculate the free energy change for the following reaction at 298 K.

$$MgCO_{3(s)} \rightarrow MgO_{(s)} + CO_{2(g)} \qquad \Delta H^{\ominus} = +117 \text{ kJmol}^{-1}, \ \Delta S^{\ominus}_{system} = +175 \text{ JK}^{-1}\text{mol}^{-1}$$

$$\Delta G = \Delta H - T\Delta S_{system} = +117 \times 10^3 - [(298 \times (+175)] = \textbf{+64 850 Jmol}^{-1}$$

ΔH must be in J not kJ. So, if you're given a value in kJ, multiply it by 10^3.

ΔG is positive — so the reaction isn't feasible at this temperature.

The Feasiblity of Some Reactions Depends on Temperature

If a reaction is exothermic (**negative ΔH**) and has a **positive entropy** change, then ΔG is **always negative** since $\Delta G = \Delta H - T\Delta S_{system}$. These reactions are feasible at **any** temperature.

If a reaction is endothermic (**positive ΔH**) and has a **negative entropy** change, then ΔG is **always positive**. These reactions are **not** feasible at any temperature.

But for other combinations, temperature has an effect.

1) If ΔH is **positive** (endothermic) and ΔS_{system} is **positive** then the reaction won't be feasible at some temperatures but **will be** at a **higher** temperature.

For example, the decomposition of **calcium carbonate** is **endothermic** but results in an **increase in entropy** (the number of molecules increases and CO_2 is a gas).

$$CaCO_{3(s)} \rightarrow CaO_{(s)} + CO_{3(g)}$$

The reaction will **only** occur when $CaCO_3$ is **heated** — it isn't feasible at 298 K.

After her surgery, Anne found that a reaction wasn't feasible.

Here's an example with numbers: $\Delta H = +10 \text{ kJ mol}^{-1}$, $\Delta S_{system} = +10 \text{ JK}^{-1}\text{mol}^{-1}$

| at **300 K** | $\Delta G = \Delta H - T\Delta S_{system}$ | $\Delta G = +10 \times 10^3 - (300 \times +10) = \textbf{+7000 J mol}^{-1}$ |
| at **1500 K** | $\Delta G = \Delta H - T\Delta S_{system}$ | $\Delta G = +10 \times 10^3 - (1500 \times +10) = \textbf{-5000 J mol}^{-1}$ |

So a reaction with these enthalpy and entropy changes is feasible at 1500 K, but not at 300 K...

2) If ΔH is **negative** (exothermic) and ΔS_{system} is **negative** then the reaction will be feasible at some temperatures but won't be **feasible** at a **higher** temperature.

For example, the process of turning **water** from a **liquid** to a **solid** is **exothermic** but results in a **decrease in entropy** (a solid is more ordered than a liquid), which means it will only occur at **certain temperatures** (i.e. at 0 °C or below).

And another example with numbers: $\Delta H = -10 \text{ kJ mol}^{-1}$, $\Delta S_{system} = -10 \text{ JK}^{-1}\text{mol}^{-1}$

| at **300 K** | $\Delta G = \Delta H - T\Delta S_{system}$ | $\Delta G = -10 \times 10^3 - (300 \times -10) = \textbf{-7000 J mol}^{-1}$ |
| at **1500 K** | $\Delta G = \Delta H - T\Delta S_{system}$ | $\Delta G = -10 \times 10^3 - (1500 \times -10) = \textbf{+5000 J mol}^{-1}$ |

...and this one is feasible at 300 K, but not at 1500 K.

Free-Energy Change

You can **Calculate** the **Temperature** at which a Reaction **Becomes Feasible**

When ΔG is **zero**, a reaction is **just feasible**.

You can find the **temperature** when ΔG is zero by rearranging the free energy equation from the previous page:

$\Delta G = \Delta H - T\Delta S_{system}$, so when $\Delta G = 0$, $T\Delta S_{system} = \Delta H$. So: $\boxed{T = \dfrac{\Delta H}{\Delta S_{system}}}$

$T =$ temperature at which a reaction becomes feasible (in K)

$\Delta H =$ enthalpy change (in $Jmol^{-1}$)

$\Delta S_{system} =$ entropy change of the system (in $JK^{-1}mol^{-1}$)

Example: Tungsten, W, can be extracted from its ore, WO_3, by reduction using hydrogen.

$$WO_{3(s)} + 3H_{2(g)} \rightarrow W_{(s)} + 3H_2O_{(g)} \qquad \Delta H^{\ominus} = +117 \text{ kJmol}^{-1}$$

Use the data in the table to find the minimum temperature at which the reaction becomes feasible.

Substance	$S^{\ominus}/ JK^{-1}mol^{-1}$
$WO_{3(s)}$	76
$H_{2(g)}$	65
$W_{(s)}$	33
$H_2O_{(g)}$	189

First, convert the **enthalpy change**, ΔH, to joules per mole:

$\Delta H = 117 \times 10^3 = \mathbf{117\,000\ Jmol^{-1}}$

Then find the **entropy change**, ΔS_{system}:

$\Delta S_{system} = S_{products} - S_{reactants} = [33 + (3 \times 189)] - [76 + (3 \times 65)] = \mathbf{+329\ JK^{-1}mol^{-1}}$

See page 67 for more on this formula.

Then divide ΔH by ΔS_{system} to find the temperature at which the reaction just becomes feasible:

$$T = \frac{\Delta H}{\Delta S_{system}} = \frac{117\,000}{329} = \mathbf{356\ K}$$

Practice Questions

Q1 What does ΔG stand for? What is it used for?

Q2 State whether each of the following reactions are feasible, feasible at certain temperatures or not feasible:
   Reaction A: negative ΔH and negative ΔS Reaction B: negative ΔH and positive ΔS
   Reaction C: positive ΔH and positive ΔS Reaction D: positive ΔH and negative ΔS

Q3 Write down the formula for calculating the temperature at which a reaction becomes feasible.

Exam Questions

1   The enthalpy change that occurs when water turns from a liquid to a solid is -6 $kJmol^{-1}$.

   $H_2O_{(l)} \rightarrow H_2O_{(s)}$ $S^{\ominus}[H_2O_{(l)}] = 70$ $JK^{-1}mol^{-1}$, $S^{\ominus}[H_2O_{(s)}] = 48$ $JK^{-1}mol^{-1}$,

   a)   Calculate the total entropy change at   (i) 250 K   (ii) 300 K   [5 marks]

   b)   Will this reaction be spontaneous at 250 K or 300 K? Explain your answer.   [2 marks]

2   Magnesium carbonate decomposes to form magnesium oxide and carbon dioxide:

   $$MgCO_{3(s)} \rightarrow MgO_{(s)} + CO_{2(g)} \qquad \Delta H^{\ominus} = +117 \text{ kJmol}^{-1} \text{ and } \Delta S^{\ominus}_{system} = +175 \text{ JK}^{-1}\text{mol}^{-1}.$$

   a)   Will this reaction occur spontaneously at a temperature of 550K?
        Explain your answer.   [2 marks]

   b)   Calculate the minimum temperature at which the reaction becomes feasible.   [2 marks]

The feasibility of revision depends on what's on the telly...

These pages are a bit confusing if you ask me — so make sure you've properly understood them before you move on. The most important bit to learn is the formula for ΔG. If you know that, then you can always work out whether a reaction is feasible even if you can't remember the rules about positive and negative enthalpy and entropy.

Period 3 Elements and Oxides

Period 3's the third row down on the Periodic Table — the one that starts with sodium and ends with argon.

Sodium is More Reactive Than Magnesium

1) **Sodium** and **magnesium** are the first two elements in **Period 3**. Sodium is in **Group 1**, and magnesium is in **Group 2**. When they react, sodium **loses one electron** to form an **Na^+ ion**, while **magnesium loses two electrons** to form **Mg^{2+}**.

2) Sodium is **more reactive** than **magnesium** because it takes **less energy** to lose **one electron** than it does to lose two. So **more energy** (usually **heat**) is needed for magnesium to react. This is shown in their reactions with **water**.

Sodium Reacts Vigorously With Water

1) Sodium reacts **vigorously** with **cold water**, forming a molten ball on the surface, fizzing and producing H_2 gas.

$$2\,Na_{(s)} + 2\,H_2O_{(l)} \rightarrow 2\,NaOH_{(aq)} + H_{2(g)}$$

2) The reaction produces **sodium hydroxide**, so forms a strongly **alkaline** solution (pH 12 – 14).

3) Magnesium reacts **very slowly** with **cold water**. You can't see any reaction, but it forms a **weakly alkaline** solution (pH 9 – 10), which shows that a reaction has occurred. The solution is only weakly alkaline because magnesium oxide is **not very soluble** in water, so relatively **few hydroxide ions** are produced.

$$Mg_{(s)} + 2\,H_2O_{(l)} \rightarrow Mg(OH)_{2(aq)} + H_{2(g)}$$

4) Magnesium reacts much faster with **steam** (i.e. when there is **more energy**), to form **magnesium oxide**.

Most Period 3 Elements React Readily With Oxygen

Period 3 elements form **oxides** when they react with **oxygen**. They're usually oxidised to their **highest** oxidation states — the same as their **group numbers**. Sulfur is the exception to this — it forms SO_2, in which it's only got a **+4** oxidation state (a **high temperature** and a **catalyst** are needed to make SO_3).

The equations are all **really similar** — element + oxygen → oxide:

P_4 is a common allotrope (form) of phosphorus.

$2Na_{(s)} + \frac{1}{2}O_{2(g)} \rightarrow Na_2O_{(s)}$ sodium oxide	$Si_{(s)} + O_{2(g)} \rightarrow SiO_{2(s)}$ silicon dioxide
$Mg_{(s)} + \frac{1}{2}O_{2(g)} \rightarrow MgO_{(s)}$ magnesium oxide	$P_{4(s)} + 5O_{2(g)} \rightarrow P_4O_{10(s)}$ phosphorus(V) oxide
$2Al_{(s)} + 1\frac{1}{2}O_{2(g)} \rightarrow Al_2O_{3(s)}$ aluminium oxide	$S_{(s)} + O_{2(g)} \rightarrow SO_{2(g)}$ sulfur dioxide

The **more reactive metals** (Na, Mg) and the **non-metals** (P, S) react **readily** in air, while **Al** and **Si** react **slowly**.

Element	Na	Mg	Al	Si	P	S
Formula of oxide	Na_2O	MgO	Al_2O_3	SiO_2	P_4O_{10}	SO_2
Reaction in air	Vigorous	Vigorous	Slow	Slow	Spontaneously combusts	Burns steadily
Flame	Yellow	Brilliant white			Brilliant white	Blue

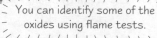

You can identify some of the oxides using flame tests.

Bonding and Structure Affect Melting Points

1) **Na_2O, MgO** and **Al_2O_3** — the metal oxides — all have **high melting points** because they form **giant ionic lattices**. The **strong forces of attraction** between each ion mean it takes a lot of heat energy to **break the bonds** and melt them.

2) MgO has a **higher melting point** than Na_2O because it forms **2+ ions**, so bonds more strongly than the 1+ ions in Na_2O.

3) Al_2O_3 has a **lower melting point** than you might expect because the 3+ ions distort the oxygen's electron cloud making the bonds **partially covalent**.

4) SiO_2 has a **higher melting point** than the other non-metal oxides because it has a **giant macromolecular** structure.

5) **P_4O_{10}** and **SO_2** have relatively **low melting points** because they form **simple molecular** structures. The molecules are bound by **weak intermolecular forces** (dipole-dipole and van der Waals), which take little energy to overcome.

Period 3 Elements and Oxides

Ionic Oxides are Alkaline, Covalent Oxides are Acidic

1) The **ionic oxides** of the **metals** Na and Mg dissolve in water to form **hydroxides**. The solutions are both **alkaline**, but **sodium hydroxide** is more soluble in water, so it forms a **more alkaline** solution than magnesium hydroxide.

$$Na_2O_{(s)} + H_2O_{(l)} \rightarrow 2NaOH_{(aq)} \quad \textbf{pH 12 - 14} \qquad MgO_{(s)} + H_2O_{(l)} \rightarrow Mg(OH)_{2(aq)} \quad \textbf{pH 9 - 10}$$

2) The **simple covalent oxides** of the **non-metals** phosphorus and sulfur form **acidic** solutions. All of the acids are **strong** and so the pH of their solutions is about **0-2**.

$$P_4O_{10(s)} + 6H_2O_{(l)} \rightarrow 4H_3PO_{4(aq)} \qquad \text{phosphoric(V) acid}$$
$$SO_{2(g)} + H_2O_{(l)} \rightarrow H_2SO_{3(aq)} \qquad \text{sulfurous acid (or sulfuric(IV) acid)}$$
$$SO_{3(l)} + H_2O_{(l)} \rightarrow H_2SO_{4(aq)} \qquad \text{sulfuric(VI) acid}$$

An ironic ox-side?

3) The **giant covalent structure** of **silicon dioxide** means that it is **insoluble** in water. However, it will **react with bases** to form salts so it is classed as **acidic**.

4) **Aluminium oxide**, which is partially **ionic** and partially **covalently** bonded, is also **insoluble** in water. But, it will react with **acids and bases** to form salts — i.e. it can act as an acid or a base, so it's classed as **amphoteric**.

Acid + Base → Salt + Water

The equation for **neutralising** an **acid** with a **base** is a classic — **acid + base → salt + water** — and it's no different for reactions of the Period 3 oxides. You may be asked to **write equations** for these reactions, so here are some examples:

① **Basic oxides neutralise acids**:
$$Na_2O_{(s)} + 2HCl_{(aq)} \rightarrow 2NaCl_{(aq)} + H_2O_{(l)}$$
$$MgO_{(s)} + H_2SO_{4(aq)} \rightarrow MgSO_{4(aq)} + H_2O_{(l)}$$

③ **Amphoteric oxides neutralise acids and bases**:
$$Al_2O_{3(s)} + 3H_2SO_{4(aq)} \rightarrow Al_2(SO_4)_{3(aq)} + 3H_2O_{(l)}$$
$$Al_2O_{3(s)} + 2NaOH_{(aq)} + 3H_2O_{(l)} \rightarrow 2NaAl(OH)_{4(aq)}$$

② **Acidic oxides neutralise bases**:
$$SiO_{2(s)} + 2NaOH_{(aq)} \rightarrow Na_2SiO_{3(aq)} + H_2O_{(l)}$$
$$P_4O_{10(s)} + 12NaOH_{(aq)} \rightarrow 4Na_3PO_{4(aq)} + 6H_2O_{(l)}$$
$$SO_{2(g)} + 2NaOH_{(aq)} \rightarrow Na_2SO_{3(aq)} + H_2O_{(l)}$$
$$SO_{3(g)} + 2NaOH_{(aq)} \rightarrow Na_2SO_{4(aq)} + H_2O_{(l)}$$

Practice Questions

Q1 Why is Na more reactive than Mg with water?

Q2 What type of oxide is: a) Na_2O,   b) P_4O_{10}.

Q3 Write an equation for the reaction of Na_2O with water.

Q4 Explain why MgO forms a less alkaline solution than Na_2O.

Exam Questions

1   X and Y are oxides of Period 3 elements.
    The Period 3 element in X has an oxidation state of +6 and the oxide forms an acidic solution in water.
    The Period 3 element in Y has an oxidation state of +1 and a high melting point.
    a)   Identify oxide X and write an equation for its reaction with water.   [2 marks]
    b)   (i) Identify oxide Y and write an equation for its reaction with water.   [2 marks]
         (ii) Explain the reason for its high melting point.   [3 marks]

2   a)   Write an equation for the formation of P_4O_{10} from phosphorus and oxygen.   [1 mark]
    b)   (i) Write an equation for the reaction between P_4O_{10} and water.   [1 mark]
         (ii) Suggest a value for the pH of the solution obtained from the reaction in part (i).   [1 mark]
    c)   Write an equation for the reaction between P_4O_{10} and potassium hydroxide.   [1 mark]

These pages have got more trends than a school disco...

Hang on a minute, I hear you cry — what about chlorine and argon? Aren't they in Period 3 too? Well, yes, they are, but you don't need to know about them. Argon's a noble gas, anyway, so it doesn't really react with anything... yawn.

Redox Equations

Redox reactions are all about the movement of electrons.

If Electrons are Transferred, it's a **Redox Reaction**

1) A **loss** of electrons is called **oxidation**. A **gain** of electrons is called **reduction**.
2) Reduction and oxidation happen **simultaneously** — hence the term '**redox**' reaction.
3) An **oxidising agent accepts** electrons and gets reduced.
4) A **reducing agent donates** electrons and gets oxidised.

$$Na + \tfrac{1}{2}Cl_2 \xrightarrow{\;-e^-\;} Na^+ Cl^-$$
$$+e^-$$

Na is oxidised
Cl is reduced

I couldn't find a red ox, so you'll have to make do with a multicoloured donkey instead.

Sometimes it's easier to talk about **Oxidation States**

(It's also called oxidation <u>number</u>.)

There are lots of rules. Take a deep breath...

1) All atoms are treated as **ions** for this, even if they're covalently bonded.

2) Uncombined **elements** have an oxidation state of **0**.

3) Elements just bonded to **identical atoms**, like O_2 and H_2, also have an oxidation state of **0**.

4) The oxidation state of a simple **monatomic ion**, e.g. Na^+, is the same as its **charge**.

5) In **compounds** or **compound ions**, the **overall oxidation state** is just the ion charge.

SO_4^{2-} — **overall oxidation state = –2**,
oxidation state of **O** = –2 (total = –8),
so oxidation state of **S** = +6

Within an ion, the most electronegative element has a negative oxidation state (equal to its ionic charge). Other elements have more positive oxidation states.

6) The sum of the oxidation states for a **neutral compound** is 0.

Fe_2O_3 — **overall oxidation state = 0**, oxidation state of **O** = –2
(total = –6), so oxidation state of **Fe** = +3

7) Combined **oxygen** is nearly always –2, except in peroxides, where it's –1,
(and in the fluorides OF_2, where it's +2, and O_2F_2, where it's +1 (and O_2 where it's 0).

In H_2O, oxidation state of **O** = –2, but in H_2O_2, oxidation state of **H** has to
be **+1** (an H atom can only lose one electron), so oxidation state of **O** = –1

8) Combined **hydrogen** is +1, except in metal hydrides where it is –1 (and H_2 where it's 0).

In **HF**, oxidation state of **H** = +1, but in **NaH**, oxidation state of **H** = –1

9) The oxidation state of a **ligand** is equivalent to the charge on the ligand. See page 82.

So the oxidation state of CN^- = **–1** and the oxidation state of NH_3 = **0**.

If you see **Roman numerals** in a chemical name, it's an **oxidation number** — it applies to the atom or group immediately before it. E.g. copper has oxidation number **+2** in **copper(II) sulfate**, and manganese has oxidation number **+7** in a **manganate(VII) ion** (MnO_4^-).

Oxidation States go **Up** or **Down** as Electrons are **Lost** or **Gained**

To work out which atoms are **oxidised** and which are **reduced** in a reaction, you need to look at the **oxidation states**.

1) The oxidation state for an atom will **increase by 1** for each **electron lost**.
2) The oxidation state will **decrease by 1** for each **electron gained**.

Example:
$$V_2O_5 + SO_2 \rightarrow V_2O_4 + SO_3$$
Oxidation state: $(+5)_{\times 2}(-2)_{\times 5} \quad (+4)(-2)_{\times 2} \quad (+4)_{\times 2}(-2)_{\times 4} \quad (+6)(-2)_{\times 3}$
V is reduced from +5 to +4 (it gains 1 electron) and **S is oxidised** from +4 to +6 (it loses two electrons).

Redox Equations

You can separate Redox Reactions into Half-Equations

1) **Ionic half-equations** show oxidation or reduction.

2) An oxidation half-equation can be **combined** with a reduction half-equation to make a **full equation**.

Example: Zinc metal displaces **silver ions** from silver nitrate solution to form **zinc nitrate** and a deposit of **silver metal**.

The zinc atoms each lose 2 electrons (oxidation) $Zn_{(s)} \rightarrow Zn^{2+}_{(aq)} + 2e^-$ ← *You need to add electrons to balance the charges on both sides.*
The silver ions each gain 1 electron (reduction) $Ag^+_{(aq)} + e^- \rightarrow Ag_{(s)}$

Two silver ions are needed to accept the **two electrons** released by each zinc atom.
So you need to double the silver half-equation before the two half-equations can be combined: $2Ag^+_{(aq)} + 2e^- \rightarrow 2Ag_{(s)}$

Now the number of electrons lost and gained **balance**, so the half-equations can be combined: $Zn_{(s)} + 2Ag^+_{(aq)} \rightarrow Zn^{2+}_{(aq)} + 2Ag_{(s)}$ *Electrons aren't included in the full equation.*

You May Need to Add H_2O and H^+ ions to Balance Half-Equations

Example: Acidified manganate(VII) ions can be reduced to Mn^{2+} by Fe^{2+} ions.
The Fe^{2+} ions are oxidised to Fe^{3+}.

Write the half-equations:

Start with the ion being reduced.	$MnO_4^-{}_{(aq)} \rightarrow Mn^{2+}_{(aq)}$
Add four water molecules to balance the oxygen.	$MnO_4^-{}_{(aq)} \rightarrow Mn^{2+}_{(aq)} + 4H_2O_{(l)}$
Then add H^+ ions to balance the hydrogen.	$MnO_4^-{}_{(aq)} + 8H^+_{(aq)} \rightarrow Mn^{2+}_{(aq)} + 4H_2O_{(l)}$
And finally, add electrons to balance the charge.	$MnO_4^-{}_{(aq)} + 8H^+_{(aq)} + 5e^- \rightarrow Mn^{2+}_{(aq)} + 4H_2O_{(l)}$
Do the same thing for the other half-equation.	$Fe^{2+}_{(aq)} \rightarrow Fe^{3+}_{(aq)} + e^-$

To balance the electrons you have to multiply the second half-equation by 5: $5Fe^{2+}_{(aq)} \rightarrow 5Fe^{3+}_{(aq)} + 5e^-$

Now you can combine both half-equations: $MnO_4^-{}_{(aq)} + 8H^+_{(aq)} + 5Fe^{2+}_{(aq)} \rightarrow Mn^{2+}_{(aq)} + 4H_2O_{(l)} + 5Fe^{3+}_{(aq)}$
Finish by checking that the charges balance: $(-1) + (+1)_{\times 8} + (+2)_{\times 5} \rightarrow (+2) + 0 + (+3)_{\times 5}$
$+17 \rightarrow +17$

Practice Questions

Q1 What is an oxidising agent?
Q2 What are you allowed to add when writing half-equations?

Exam Questions

1   What is the oxidation number of the following elements?
   a) Ti in $TiCl_4$ b) V in V_2O_5 c) Cr in CrO_4^{2-} d) Cr in $Cr_2O_7^{2-}$ [4 marks]

2   Dichromate ions ($Cr_2O_7^{2-}$) are reduced to Cr^{3+} ions by zinc. Zinc is oxidised during this process.
   Write ionic half-equations to show the reduction and oxidation processes.   [2 marks]

3   Acidified manganate(VII) ions will react with aqueous iodide ions to form iodine.
   The two half-equations for the changes that occur are:
     $MnO_4^-{}_{(aq)} + 8H^+_{(aq)} + 5e^- \rightarrow Mn^{2+}_{(aq)} + 4H_2O_{(l)}$ and $2I^-_{(aq)} \rightarrow I_{2(aq)} + 2e^-$
   a) Write the balanced equation to show the reaction taking place.   [2 marks]
   b) Use oxidation numbers to explain the redox processes which have occurred.   [4 marks]
   c) Suggest why a fairly reactive metal such as zinc will not react with aqueous iodide ions in a
     similar manner to manganate(VII) ions.   [2 marks]

Oxidise what? You'll have to speak to my agent...

*The words oxidation and reduction are tossed about a lot in chemistry — so they're important.
Don't forget, oxidation is really about electrons being lost, **not** oxygen being gained, but you'll
hopefully remember that from AS. Here's that memory aid thingy again just in case...*

OIL RIG
- **O**xidation **I**s **L**oss
- **R**eduction **I**s **G**ain
(of electrons)

Electrode Potentials

There's electrons toing and froing in redox reactions. And when electrons move, you get electricity.

Electrochemical Cells Make Electricity

Electrochemical cells can be made from **two different metals** dipped in salt solutions of their **own ions** and connected by a wire (the **external circuit**).

There are always **two** reactions within an electrochemical cell — one's an oxidation and one's a reduction — so it's a **redox process** (see page 72).

Here's what happens in the **zinc/copper** electrochemical cell on the right:

1) Zinc **loses electrons** more easily than copper. So in the half-cell on the left, zinc (from the zinc electrode) is **OXIDISED** to form $Zn^{2+}_{(aq)}$ ions. This releases electrons into the external circuit.

2) In the other half-cell, the **same number of electrons** are taken from the external circuit, **REDUCING** the Cu^{2+} ions to copper atoms.

The solutions are connected by a **salt bridge** made from filter paper soaked in $KNO_{3(aq)}$. This allows ions to flow through and balance out the charges.

So **electrons** flow through the wire from the most reactive metal to the least.

A voltmeter in the external circuit shows the **voltage** between the two half-cells. This is the **cell potential** or **e.m.f.**, E_{cell}.

The boys tested the strength of the bridge, whilst the girls just stood and watched.

You can also have half-cells involving **solutions of two aqueous ions of the same element**, such as $Fe^{2+}_{(aq)}/Fe^{3+}_{(aq)}$.

The conversion from Fe^{2+} to Fe^{3+}, or vice versa, happens on the surface of the **electrode**.

The electrode is made of **platinum** because it is an **inert metal**.

The Reactions at Each Electrode are Reversible

1) The **reactions** that occur at each electrode in the **zinc/copper cell** above are:

$$Zn^{2+}_{(aq)} + 2e^- \rightleftharpoons Zn_{(s)}$$
$$Cu^{2+}_{(aq)} + 2e^- \rightleftharpoons Cu_{(s)}$$

2) The **reversible arrows** show that both reactions can go in **either direction**. **Which direction** each reaction goes in depends on **how easily** each metal **loses electrons** (i.e. how easily it's **oxidised**).

3) How easily a metal is oxidised is measured using **electrode potentials**. A metal that's **easily oxidised** has a very **negative electrode potential**, while one that's harder to oxidise has a less negative or **positive electrode potential**.

Half-cell	Electrode potential (V)
$Zn^{2+}_{(aq)}/Zn_{(s)}$	−0.76
$Cu^{2+}_{(aq)}/Cu_{(s)}$	+0.34

4) The table on the left shows the electrode potentials for the copper and zinc half-cells. The **zinc half-cell** has a **more negative** electrode potential, so **zinc is oxidised** (the reaction goes **backwards**), while **copper is reduced** (the reaction goes **forwards**).

There's a Convention for Drawing Electrochemical Cells

It's a bit of a faff drawing pictures of electrochemical cells. There's a **shorthand** way of representing them though — this is the **Zn/Cu cell**:

There are a couple of important **conventions** when drawing cells:

1) The **half-cell** with the **more negative** potential goes on the **left**.

2) The **oxidised forms** go in the **centre** of the cell diagram.

$$Zn_{(s)} \mid Zn^{2+}_{(aq)} \parallel Cu^{2+}_{(aq)} \mid Cu_{(s)}$$

Changes go in this direction

| reduced form | oxidised form | oxidised form | reduced form |

If you follow the conventions, you can **calculate** the **cell potential** by doing the calculation:

$$E^\ominus_{cell} = \left(E^\ominus_{\text{right hand side}} - E^\ominus_{\text{left hand side}}\right)$$

The symbol for electrode potential is $E^\ominus$.

The cell potential will always be a **positive voltage**, because the more negative $E^\ominus$ value is being subtracted from the more positive $E^\ominus$ value. For example, the cell potential for the Zn/Cu cell = $+0.34 - (-0.76) = \mathbf{+1.10\,V}$

Electrode Potentials

Conditions Affect the Value of the Electrode Potential

Half-cell reactions are **reversible**. So just like any other reversible reaction, the **equilibrium position** is affected by changes in **temperature**, **pressure** and **concentration**. Changing the equilibrium position changes the **cell potential**. To get around this, **standard conditions** are used to measure electrode potentials — using these conditions means you always get the **same value** for the electrode potential and you can **compare values** for different cells.

Electrode Potentials are Measured Against Standard Hydrogen Electrodes

You measure the electrode potential of a half-cell against a **standard hydrogen electrode**.

> The **standard electrode potential** of a half-cell is the **voltage measured** under **standard conditions** when the **half-cell** is connected to a **standard hydrogen electrode**.

Standard conditions are:
1) Any solution must have a concentration of 1.00 moldm⁻³.
2) The temperature must be 298 K (25 °C).
3) The pressure must be 100 kPa.

$$Pt \mid H_{2(g)} \mid H^+_{(aq)} \parallel Zn^{2+}_{(aq)} \mid Zn_{(s)}$$

This is the cell drawn conventionally. The platinum electrode is shown, but it doesn't take part in the reaction.

1) The **standard hydrogen electrode** is always shown on the **left** — it doesn't matter whether or not the other half-cell has a more positive value. The standard hydrogen electrode half-cell has an electrode potential of **0.00 V**.

2) The whole cell potential = $E^{\ominus}_{\text{right-hand side}} - E^{\ominus}_{\text{left-hand side}}$.

   $E^{\ominus}_{\text{left-hand side}} = 0.00$ V, so the **voltage reading** will be equal to $E^{\ominus}_{\text{right-hand side}}$.
   This reading could be **positive** or **negative**, depending which way the **electrons flow**.

Practice Questions

Q1 Draw the cell used for determining the value of $E^{\ominus}$ for the Fe^{3+}/Fe^{2+} system using the conventional representation.

Q2 $Fe^{3+} + e^- \rightleftharpoons Fe^{2+}$, $E^{\ominus} = +0.77$ V $\qquad$ $Mn^{3+} + e^- \rightleftharpoons Mn^{2+}$, $E^{\ominus} = +1.48$ V
Show that the e.m.f. of an iron/manganese cell under standard conditions is +0.71 V.

Q3 List the three standard conditions used when measuring standard electrode potentials.

Exam Question

1 An electrochemical cell containing a zinc half-cell and a silver half-cell was set up using a potassium nitrate salt bridge. The cell potential at 25 °C was measured to be 1.40 V.

$$Zn^{2+}_{(aq)} + 2e^- \rightleftharpoons Zn_{(s)} \qquad E^{\ominus} = -0.76 \text{ V}$$
$$Ag^+_{(aq)} + e^- \rightleftharpoons Ag_{(s)} \qquad E^{\ominus} = +0.80 \text{ V}$$

a) Draw this cell using the conventional representation. [2 marks]

b) Use the standard electrode potentials given to calculate the standard cell potential for a zinc-silver cell. [1 mark]

c) Suggest two possible reasons why the actual cell potential was different from the value calculated in part (b). [2 marks]

d) Write an equation for the overall cell reaction. [1 mark]

e) Which half-cell released the electrons into the circuit? Explain how you know this. [1 mark]

Like greased lightning — IT'S ELECTRIFYING...

You've just got to think long and hard about this stuff. The metal on the left-hand electrode disappears off into the solution, leaving its electrons behind. This makes the left-hand electrode the negative one. So the right-hand electrode's got to be the positive one. It makes sense if you think about it. This electrode gives up electrons to turn the positive ions into atoms.

Electrochemical Series

Elements have different standard electrode potentials. So what do chemists do — they write a list of them all in order.

Cells Provide **Evidence** that Electrons are Transferred

1) **Redox reactions** involve the **transfer of electrons** from one substance to another — or so the **theory** goes. But you might wonder **how** anyone knows this — you **can't see** the electrons move.

2) What you can do is use the **theory** to make a **prediction**, and then **test** the prediction with an **experiment**. For example, you could predict that a **current** will flow between the electrodes of an **electrochemical cell** if an **oxidation** reaction happens at one electrode and a **reduction** at the other electrode.

3) And **a current does flow** — you can even stick an ammeter in the circuit and measure it. So, the electrochemical cell **provides evidence** that **electrons are transferred** in redox reactions.

4) Don't forget that an experiment **doesn't prove** a theory — someone, someday might do an experiment that shows electrons aren't transferred in chemical reactions. That seems **unlikely** at the moment because all the **evidence** we have **fits the theory** that electrons are transferred. So for now that's the theory that chemists are sticking to.

The **Electrochemical Series** Shows You What's **Reactive** and What's Not

1) The **more reactive** a **metal** is, the **more** it wants to **lose electrons** to form a **positive ion**. **More reactive metals** have **more negative** standard electrode potentials.

> **Example:** Magnesium is **more reactive** than zinc — so it's more eager to form 2+ ions than zinc is.
> The list of standard electrode potentials shows that Mg^{2+}/Mg has a **more negative** value than Zn^{2+}/Zn.
> In terms of oxidation and reduction, magnesium would **reduce** Zn^{2+} (or Zn^{2+} would **oxidise** magnesium).

2) The more reactive a **non-metal** the **more** it wants to **gain electrons** to form a **negative ion**. **More reactive non-metals** have **more positive** standard electrode potentials.

> **Example:** Chlorine is **more reactive** than bromine — so it's more eager to form a negative ion than bromine is.
> The list of standard electrode potentials shows that $Cl_2/2Cl^-$ is **more positive** than $Br_2/2Br^-$.
> In terms of oxidation and reduction, chlorine would **oxidise** Br^- (or Br^- would **reduce** chlorine).

3) Here's an **electrochemical series** showing some standard electrode potentials:

Half-reaction	E°/V
$Mg^{2+}_{(aq)} + 2e^- \rightleftharpoons Mg_{(s)}$	−2.38
$Al^{3+}_{(aq)} + 3e^- \rightleftharpoons Al_{(s)}$	−1.66
$Zn^{2+}_{(aq)} + 2e^- \rightleftharpoons Zn_{(s)}$	−0.76
$Ni^{2+}_{(aq)} + 2e^- \rightleftharpoons Ni_{(s)}$	−0.25
$2H^+_{(aq)} + 2e^- \rightleftharpoons H_{2(g)}$	0.00
$Sn^{4+}_{(aq)} + 2e^- \rightleftharpoons Sn^{2+}_{(aq)}$	+0.15
$Cu^{2+}_{(aq)} + 2e^- \rightleftharpoons Cu_{(s)}$	+0.34
$Fe^{3+}_{(aq)} + e^- \rightleftharpoons Fe^{2+}_{(aq)}$	+0.77
$Ag^+_{(aq)} + e^- \rightleftharpoons Ag_{(s)}$	+0.80
$Br_{2(aq)} + 2e^- \rightleftharpoons 2Br^-_{(aq)}$	+1.07
$Cr_2O_7^{2-}_{(aq)} + 14H^+_{(aq)} + 6e^- \rightleftharpoons 2Cr^{3+}_{(aq)} + 7H_2O_{(l)}$	+1.33
$Cl_{2(aq)} + 2e^- \rightleftharpoons 2Cl^-_{(aq)}$	+1.36
$MnO_4^-_{(aq)} + 8H^+_{(aq)} + 5e^- \rightleftharpoons Mn^{2+}_{(aq)} + 4H_2O_{(l)}$	+1.52

Chestnut wondered if his load was hindering his pulling potential.

More negative electrode potentials mean that:
1. The right-hand substances are more easily oxidised (they lose electrons more easily).
2. The left-hand substances are more stable.

More positive electrode potentials mean that:
1. The left-hand substances are more easily reduced (they gain electrons more easily).
2. The right-hand substances are more stable.

Electrochemical Series

The **Anticlockwise Rule** Predicts Whether a Reaction Will Happen

You can use the **anticlockwise rule** to **predict** whether a reaction will occur and to show which **direction** it will go in.

For example, will zinc react with aqueous copper ions?

First you write the two half-equations down, putting the one with the **more negative** standard electrode potential on **top**. In each equation, the **oxidised** state of the substance goes on the **left** and the **reduced** state on the **right**. Then you draw on some **anticlockwise arrows** — these give you the **direction** of each half-reaction.

oxidised states $\begin{cases} Zn^{2+}_{(aq)} + 2e^- \rightleftharpoons Zn_{(s)} \\ Cu^{2+}_{(aq)} + 2e^- \rightleftharpoons Cu_{(s)} \end{cases}$ reduced states $E^\circ = -0.76 \text{ V}$
$E^\circ = +0.34 \text{ V}$

The **half-equations** are: $Zn_{(s)} \rightleftharpoons Zn^{2+}_{(aq)} + 2e^-$
$Cu^{2+}_{(aq)} + 2e^- \rightleftharpoons Cu_{(s)}$

Which combine to give: $Zn_{(s)} + Cu^{2+}_{(aq)} \rightleftharpoons Zn^{2+}_{(aq)} + Cu_{(s)}$

So zinc **does** react with aqueous copper ions.

To find the **cell potential** you do $E^\circ_{bottom} - E^\circ_{top}$, so the cell potential for this reaction is $+0.34 - (-0.76) = +1.10 \text{ V}$.

The anticlockwise rule shows that **no reaction** happens if your solution contains Zn^{2+} ions and Cu metal — you can't draw anticlockwise arrows from these substances. You can use the rule to work out whether any two substances will react — just remember to put the half-cell with the **more negative** standard electrode potential on the **top**.

Practice Questions

Q1 Cu is less reactive than Pb.
Which half-reaction has a more negative standard electrode potential, $Pb^{2+} + 2e^- \rightleftharpoons Pb$ or $Cu^{2+} + 2e^- \rightleftharpoons Cu$?

Q2 Use electrode potentials to show that magnesium will reduce Zn^{2+}.

Q3 What is the anticlockwise rule used for? Outline how you use it.

Q4 Use the table on the opposite page to predict whether or not Zn^{2+} ions can oxidise Fe^{2+} ions to Fe^{3+} ions.

Exam Questions

1   Use E° values quoted on the opposite page to determine the outcome of mixing the following solutions.
   If there is a reaction, determine the E° value and write the equation. If there isn't a reaction, state this and explain why.
   a) Zinc metal and Ni^{2+} ions   [2 marks]

   b) Acidified MnO_4^- ions and Sn^{2+} ions   [2 marks]

   c) $Br_{2(aq)}$ and acidified $Cr_2O_7^{2-}$ ions   [2 marks]

   d) Silver ions and Fe^{2+} ions   [2 marks]

2   Use the following data to answer the questions below.
   $O_{2(g)} + 2H_2O_{(l)} + 4e^- \rightleftharpoons 4OH^-_{(aq)}$ $E^\circ = +0.40 \text{ V}$
   $Fe^{2+}_{(aq)} + 2e^- \rightleftharpoons Fe_{(s)}$ $E^\circ = -0.44 \text{ V}$

   a) (i) Draw a cell diagram for the reaction using the conventional representation.   [1 mark]

      (ii) Calculate the e.m.f. for the cell.   [1 mark]

   b) Use electrode potentials to explain why iron is oxidised in the presence of oxygen and water. [1 mark]

The forward reaction that happens is the one with the most positive $E^\ominus$ value...

To see if a reaction will happen, you basically find the two half-equations in the electrochemical series and check whether you can draw anticlockwise arrows on them to get from your reactants to your products. If you can — great. The reaction will have a positive electrode potential, so it should happen. If you can't — well, it ain't gonna work.

Electrochemical Cells

It turns out that electrochemical cells aren't just found in the lab — they're all over your house too... read on.

Electrochemical Cells Are Used as Batteries

The **batteries** that we use to power everything from watches to digital cameras and mobile phones are all types of **electrochemical cell**. Some types of cell are **rechargeable** while others can only be used until they **run out**.

Non-Rechargeable Cells use Irreversible Reactions

A common type of non-rechargeable cell is a **dry cell alkaline battery**. You'll probably find some of these in the TV remote control, torch or smoke alarms in your house. They're useful for gadgets that **don't** use a lot of **power** or are only used for **short periods** of time.

For example, **zinc-carbon dry cell batteries** have a **zinc anode** and a **mixture of manganese dioxide and carbon** for a **cathode**. In between the electrodes is a paste of **ammonium chloride**, which acts as an **electrolyte**.

The **half-equations** are:

$$Zn_{(s)} \rightarrow Zn^{2+}_{(aq)} + 2e^- \qquad\qquad E^\circ = -0.76 \text{ V}$$

$$2MnO_{2(s)} + 2NH_4^+{}_{(aq)} + 2e^- \rightarrow Mn_2O_{3(s)} + 2NH_{3(aq)} + H_2O_{(l)} \qquad E^\circ = +0.75 \text{ V}$$

So the **cell** is drawn as: $\quad Zn_{(s)} \mid Zn^{2+}_{(aq)} \mid\mid MnO_{2(s)} \mid Mn_2O_{3(s)}$

The **e.m.f.** of this type of cell is: $\quad E^\circ_{cell} = (E^\circ_{\text{right hand side}} - E^\circ_{\text{left hand side}})$

You draw the cell and calculate the e.m.f. in exactly the same way as for any other electrochemical cell.

$$= +0.75 - (-0.76) = +1.51 \text{ V}$$

The half-equations have **non-reversible arrows** because it is **not practical** to reverse them in a battery. They can be made to run backwards under the **right conditions**, but trying to do this in a **battery** can make it **leak** or **explode**. This is because the **zinc anode** forms the **casing** of the battery, so becomes **thinner** as the zinc is **oxidised**.

Another reason why these batteries **cannot be recharged** is that the ammonium ions produce **hydrogen gas**, which **escapes** from the battery. Without the hydrogen, the ammonium ions **cannot be reformed** by reversing the reactions.

Rechargeable Cells use Reversible Reactions

Rechargeable batteries are found in loads of devices, such as **mobile phones**, **laptops** and **cars**.

For example, **lead-acid cells** are used in car batteries. They normally consist of **6 cells** connected in series. Each cell is made up of a **lead(IV) dioxide anode** and a **lead cathode** immersed in a **sulfuric acid** electrolyte. Both electrodes end up coated in **lead(II) sulfate**.

The half-equations are:

$$Pb_{(s)} + SO_4^{2-}{}_{(aq)} \rightleftharpoons PbSO_{4(s)} + 2e^- \qquad\qquad E^\circ = -0.36 \text{ V}$$

$$PbO_{2(s)} + SO_4^{2-}{}_{(aq)} + 4H^+{}_{(aq)} + 2e^- \rightleftharpoons PbSO_{4(s)} + 2H_2O_{(l)} \qquad E^\circ = +1.69 \text{ V}$$

So the cell is drawn as: $\quad Pb_{(s)} \mid PbSO_{4(s)} \mid\mid PbSO_{4(s)} \mid PbO_{2(s)}$

The **e.m.f.** of this type of cell is: $E^\circ_{cell} = (E^\circ_{\text{right hand side}} - E^\circ_{\text{left hand side}}) = +1.69 - (-0.36) = +2.05 \text{ V}$

Two other types of rechargeable battery are **NiCad (nickel-cadmium)** and **L ion (lithium ion)**. To recharge these batteries, a **current** is supplied to force **electrons** to flow in the **opposite direction** around the circuit and **reverse the reactions**. This is possible because **none of the substances** in a rechargeable battery **escape** or are **used up**.

Non-Rechargeable Batteries Have Advantages and Disadvantages

1) **Cost**: non-rechargeable batteries are **cheaper** than rechargeables to buy. However, non-rechargeable batteries have to be **replaced** every time they run out, so **rechargeables are cheaper in the long run**.

2) **Lifetime**: a non-rechargeable battery will **work for longer** than a rechargeable battery. But once a rechargeable battery has run out, you can **recharge it** and use it again whereas non-rechargeables have to be **disposed** of.

3) **Power**: non-rechargeable batteries **can't supply as much power** as rechargeables, so are **no use** in devices that use a **lot of power** — like a mobile phone or a laptop.

4) **Use of resources and waste**: more non-rechargeable batteries are produced because they can only be used once, which **uses more resources** and means they create **more waste** than rechargeables. Both types of battery can be **recycled** and the metals in them recovered to use again, but often we just chuck them in the bin and they end up in **landfill**.

5) **Toxicity**: non-rechargeable batteries are **less likely** to contain the **toxic metals lead** and **cadmium** (although they may contain **mercury**), so they are less hazardous in landfill if the contents **leak** out and **pollute water sources**.

Electrochemical Cells

Fuel Cells can Generate Electricity From Hydrogen and Oxygen

In most cells the **chemicals** that generate the electricity are contained in the **electrodes** and the **electrolyte** that form the cell. In a fuel cell the chemicals are **stored separately** outside the cell and fed in when electricity is required. One example of this is the **hydrogen-oxygen fuel cell**, which can be used to **power electric vehicles**.

Hydrogen and **oxygen gases** are fed into two separate platinum-containing electrodes. The electrodes are separated by an **ion-exchange membrane** that **allows protons** (H^+ ions) to pass through it, but **stops electrons** going through it.

Hydrogen is fed to the **negative electrode**.
The **reaction** that occurs is:

$$2H_2 \rightarrow 4H^+ + 4e^-$$

The **electrons** flow from the **negative electrode** through an **external circuit** to the **positive electrode**. The H^+ ions pass through the **ion-exchange membrane** towards the positive electrode.

Oxygen is fed to the positive electrode.
The **reaction** here is:

$$O_2 + 4H^+ + 4e^- \rightarrow 2H_2O$$

The **overall effect** is that H_2 and O_2 react to make **water**:

$$2H_2 + O_2 \rightarrow 2H_2O$$

Fuel Cells Don't Need Recharging

The **major advantage** of fuel cells over batteries is that they **don't need electrical recharging**. As long as **hydrogen** and **oxygen** are supplied, the cell will continue to **produce electricity**. Another benefit is that the only **waste product** is **water**, so there are **no nasty toxic chemicals** to dispose of and **no CO_2 emissions** from the cell itself.

The **downside** is that you **need energy** to produce a supply of **hydrogen** and **oxygen**. They can be produced from the **electrolysis of water** — i.e. by **reusing the waste product** from the fuel cell, but this requires **electricity** — and this **electricity** is normally generated by **burning fossil fuels**. So the whole process isn't usually carbon neutral. **Hydrogen** is also **highly flammable** so it needs to be handled carefully when it is **stored** or **transported**.

Practice Questions

Q1 Explain the difference between non-rechargeable and rechargeable batteries in terms of the chemical reactions.

Q2 Give one advantage of non-rechargeable batteries.

Q3 Describe a possible environmental problem caused by rechargeable batteries.

Q4 What metal is used in the electrodes in a hydrogen-oxygen fuel cell?

Exam Questions

1 Simple cells can be created from the following half-cells.

Half-cell (1)	$Cu^{2+}_{(aq)} + 2e^- \rightleftharpoons Cu_{(s)}$	$E^\circ = +0.34$ V
Half-cell (2)	$Mg^{2+}_{(aq)} + 2e^- \rightleftharpoons Mg_{(s)}$	$E^\circ = -2.38$ V
Half-cell (3)	$Zn^{2+}_{(aq)} + 2e^- \rightleftharpoons Zn_{(s)}$	$E^\circ = -0.76$ V

Calculate the E° cell value for cells formed between:

a) half-cells (1) and (2) [1 mark]

b) half-cells (1) and (3) [1 mark]

2 This question is about the hydrogen-oxygen fuel cell.

a) (i) Write a half-equation for the reaction of oxygen gas at the positive electrode. [1 mark]

(ii) Where do the electrons come from in this reaction? [1 mark]

b) State one advantage and one disadvantage of hydrogen fuel cells. [2 marks]

Why is chemistry revision like a good battery? It just keeps on going...

You've got to love batteries — they sit there in their shiny metal cases all ready to release the energy stored inside them just when you need it most. So, have some respect for batteries and don't just throw them in the bin when they go flat, recharge them if you can, and if not recycle them. Oh, and you'd probably best learn those half-equations too.

Transition Metals — The Basics

This section's all about transition metals — and there's a lot of it. It's obviously important stuff in the A2 chemistry world.

Transition Elements are Found in the d-Block

The **d-block** is the block of elements in the middle of the periodic table. Most of the elements in the d-block are **transition elements** (or transition metals).

You mainly need to know about the ones in the first row of the d-block. These are the elements from **titanium to copper**.

The Electronic Configurations of Transition Metals Cause Their Properties

Here's the definition of a transition metal:

> A **transition metal** is a metal that can form **one or more stable ions** with a **partially filled d-subshell**.

A d-orbital can fit **10** electrons in. So transition metals must form **at least one ion** that has **between 1 and 9 electrons** in the d-orbital. All the Period 4 d-block elements are transition metals apart from **scandium** and **zinc**. Here are their electronic configurations:

The 3d orbitals are occupied singly at first. They only double up when they have to.

The 4s orbital usually fills up first.

Chromium prefers to have one electron in each orbital of the 3d subshell and just one in the 4s subshell — this gives it more stability.

Copper prefers to have a full 3d subshell and just one electron in the 4s subshell — it's more stable that way.

It's the incomplete d-subshell that causes the **special chemical properties** of transition metals on the next page.

Sc and Zn Aren't Transition Metals

Scandium only forms one ion, **Sc^{3+}**, which has an **empty d-subshell**. Scandium has the electronic configuration **$[Ar]3d^14s^2$**, so when it loses three electrons to form Sc^{3+}, it ends up with the electronic configuration **[Ar]**.

Zinc only forms one ion, **Zn^{2+}**, which has a **full d-subshell**. Zinc has the electronic configuration **$[Ar]3d^{10}4s^2$**. When it forms Zn^{2+} it loses 2 electrons, both from the 4s subshell. This means it keeps its full 3d subshell.

When Ions are Formed, the s Electrons are Removed First

Transition metal atoms form **positive** ions. When this happens, the **s electrons** are removed **first**, **then** the d electrons.

For example, iron forms Fe^{2+} ions and Fe^{3+} ions.
When it forms 2+ ions, it loses **both its 4s electrons. Fe = $[Ar]3d^6 4s^2 \rightarrow Fe^{2+} = [Ar]3d^6$**
Only once the 4s electrons are removed can a **3d electron** be removed. E.g. **$Fe^{2+} = [Ar]3d^6 \rightarrow Fe^{3+} = [Ar]3d^5$**

Transition Metals — The Basics

The Transition Metals All Have Similar Physical Properties

The transition elements don't gradually change across the periodic table like you might expect. They're all typical metals and have **similar physical properties**:

> 1) They all have a **high density**.
> 2) They all have **high melting** and **high boiling points**.
> 3) Their **ionic radii** are more or less the same.

Transition Metals Have Special Chemical Properties

1) They can form **complex ions** — see pages 82-83. E.g. iron forms a **complex ion with water** — $[Fe(H_2O)_6]^{2+}$.

2) They form **coloured ions** — see pages 84-85. E.g. Fe^{2+} ions are **pale green** and Fe^{3+} ions are **yellow**.

3) They're **good catalysts** — see pages 90-91. E.g. iron is the catalyst used in the **Haber process**.

4) They can exist in **variable oxidation states** — see pages 86-87. E.g. iron can exist in the **+2** oxidation state as Fe^{2+} ions and in the **+3** oxidation state as Fe^{3+} ions.

Some common **coloured** ions and **oxidation states** are shown below. The colours refer to the **aqueous ions**.

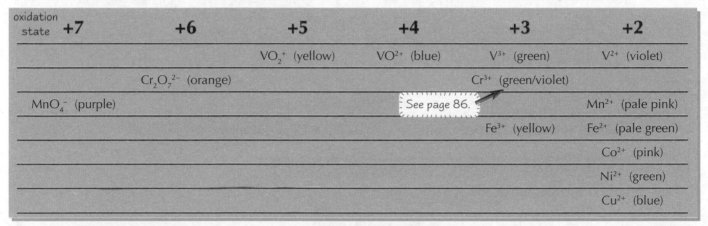

oxidation state +7	+6	+5	+4	+3	+2
		VO_2^+ (yellow)	VO^{2+} (blue)	V^{3+} (green)	V^{2+} (violet)
	$Cr_2O_7^{2-}$ (orange)			Cr^{3+} (green/violet)	
MnO_4^- (purple)			*See page 86.*		Mn^{2+} (pale pink)
				Fe^{3+} (yellow)	Fe^{2+} (pale green)
					Co^{2+} (pink)
					Ni^{2+} (green)
					Cu^{2+} (blue)

These elements show **variable** oxidation states because the **energy levels** of the 4s and the 3d subshells are **very close** to one another. So different numbers of electrons can be gained or lost using fairly **similar** amounts of energy.

Practice Questions

Q1 Give the electronic arrangement of: (a) a vanadium atom, (b) a V^{2+} ion.

Q2 What is the definition of a transition metal?

Q3 State four chemical properties which are characteristic of transition elements.

Exam Questions

1 When solid copper(I) sulfate is added to water, a blue solution forms with a red-brown precipitate of copper metal.
 a) Give the electron configuration of copper(I) ions. [1 mark]
 b) Does the formation of copper(I) ions show copper acting as a transition metal? Explain your answer. [2 marks]
 c) Identify the blue solution. [1 mark]

2 V^{3+} can be oxidised to VO_2^+ by MnO_4^- in acid solution. The MnO_4^- is reduced to Mn^{2+}.
 a) What is the oxidation state of vanadium in VO_2^+? [1 mark]
 b) Write balanced half-equations for:
  (i) the reduction of MnO_4^- to Mn^{2+} (ii) the oxidation of V^{3+} to VO_2^+ [4 marks]
 c) Combine the two half-equations to make a balanced equation for the reaction. [2 marks]

s electrons — like rats leaving a sinking ship...

Definitely have a quick read of the electronic configuration stuff in your AS notes if it's been pushed to a little corner of your mind labelled, "Well, I won't be needing that again in a hurry". It should come flooding back pretty quickly. This page is just an overview of transition metal properties. Don't worry — they're all looked at in lots more detail in the coming pages...

Complex Ions

Transition metals are always forming complex ions. These aren't as complicated as they sound, though. Honest.

Complex Ions are Metal Ions Surrounded by Ligands

A **complex** is a **metal ion** surrounded by **coordinately bonded ligands**.

1) A **coordinate bond** (or dative covalent bond) is a covalent bond in which **both electrons** in the shared pair come from the **same atom**. In a complex, they come from the **ligands**.

2) So, a **ligand** is an atom, ion or molecule that **donates a pair of electrons** to a central metal ion.

3) The **coordination number** is the **number** of **coordinate bonds** that are formed with the central metal ion.

4) The usual coordination numbers are **6** and **4**. If the ligands are **small**, like H_2O or NH_3, **6** can fit around the central metal ion. But if the ligands are **larger**, like Cl^-, **only 4** can fit around the central metal ion.

6 COORDINATE BONDS MEAN AN OCTAHEDRAL SHAPE

Here are a few examples.

The ligands don't have to be all the same.

$[Fe(H_2O)_6]^{2+}_{(aq)}$ $[Co(NH_3)_6]^{3+}_{(aq)}$ $[Cu(NH_3)_4(H_2O)_2]^{2+}_{(aq)}$

The different types of **bond arrow** show that the complex is **3-D**. The **wedge-shaped arrows** represent bonds coming **towards you** and the **dashed arrows** represent bonds **sticking out behind** the molecule.

4 COORDINATE BONDS USUALLY MEAN A TETRAHEDRAL SHAPE...

E.g. $[CuCl_4]^{2-}$, which is yellow, and $[CoCl_4]^{2-}$, which is blue.

...BUT NOT ALWAYS

In a **few** complexes, e.g. **cisplatin** (shown on the right), **4 coordinate bonds** form a **square planar** shape.

SOME SILVER COMPLEXES HAVE 2 COORDINATE BONDS AND FORM A LINEAR SHAPE

$[Ag(NH_3)_2]^+$ forms a **linear shape**, as shown.

$$\left[H_3N\!:\!\longrightarrow\!Ag\!\longleftarrow\!:\!NH_3 \right]^+$$

See page 92 for the uses of $[Ag(NH_3)_2]^+$ and cisplatin.

Complex Ions Have an Overall Charge or Total Oxidation State

The **overall charge** on the complex ion is its **total oxidation state**. It's put **outside** the **square** brackets. For example:

$[Cu(H_2O)_6]^{2+}_{(aq)}$ Overall charge is 2+.

You have to know how to work out the **oxidation state of the metal**:

> The oxidation state of the metal ion   =   the total oxidation state − the sum of the oxidation states of the ligands

E.g. $[CoCl_4]^{2-}_{(aq)}$ The total oxidation state is **−2** and each Cl^- ligand has an oxidation state of **−1**. So in this complex, cobalt's oxidation state $= -2 - (4 \times -1) = \textbf{+2}$.

Complex Ions

A Ligand Must Have at Least One Lone Pair of Electrons

A ligand must have **at least one lone pair of electrons**, or it won't have anything to use to form a **coordinate bond**.

1) Ligands with **one lone pair** are called **unidentate** — e.g. $H_2\ddot{O}$, $\ddot{N}H_3$, $\ddot{C}\ddot{l}^-$.

2) Ligands with **more than one lone pair** are called **multidentate** — e.g. $EDTA^{4-}$ has six lone pairs (it's **hexadentate** to be precise) so it can form **six coordinate bonds** with a metal ion.

3) **Bidentate** ligands are multidentate ligands with **two lone pairs** — e.g. ethane-1,2-diamine, $\ddot{N}H_2CH_2CH_2\ddot{N}H_2$. Bidentate ligands can each form **two coordinate bonds** with a metal ion.

Each **ethane-1,2-diamine** molecule has 2 lone pairs and forms **2 coordinate bonds** with the metal ion.

The $EDTA^{4-}$ ion has 6 lone pairs, so it forms **6 coordinate bonds** with the metal ion.

Haem in Haemoglobin Contains a Multidentate Ligand

1) **Haemoglobin** is a protein found in **blood** that helps to **transport oxygen** around the body.

2) **Haemoglobin** contains Fe^{2+} ions, which are **hexa-coordinated** — **six lone pairs** are donated to them to form **six coordinate bonds**.

3) **Four** of the lone pairs come from **nitrogen atoms**, which form a **circle** around the Fe^{2+}. This part of the molecule is called **haem**.

4) The **molecule** that the **four nitrogen atoms** are part of is a **multidentate ligand**.

5) A protein called **globin** and either an **oxygen** or a **water** molecule also bind to the to the Fe^{2+} ion to form an **octahedral structure**. (See page 91 for more on haemoglobin.)

Practice Questions

Q1 What is meant by the term 'complex ion'?

Q2 Describe how a ligand, such as ammonia, bonds to a central metal ion.

Q3 What is meant by the term 'bidentate ligand'? Give an example of one.

Q4 Draw the shape of the complex ion $[Co(NH_3)_6]^{3+}$. Name the shape.

Exam Questions

1   a)   Using $[Ag(NH_3)_2]^+$ as an example, explain what is meant by the following terms:
        (i)   ligand   [2 marks]
        (ii) coordinate bond   [2 marks]
        (iii) coordination number   [2 marks]
    b) $S_2O_3^{2-}$ is a unidentate ligand. What shape is $[Ag(S_2O_3)_2]^{3-}$?   [1 mark]

2   When concentrated hydrochloric acid is added to an aqueous solution of $Cu^{2+}_{(aq)}$ a yellow solution is formed.
    a)   State the coordination number and shape of the $Cu^{2+}_{(aq)}$ complex ion in the **initial solution**.   [2 marks]
    b)   State the coordination number, shape and formula of the complex ion responsible for the yellow solution. [3 marks]
    c)   Explain why the coordination number is different in the yellow solution.   [2 marks]

3   a)   Write an equation for the complete replacement of the water ligands in $[Co(H_2O)_6]^{2+}$ with ethane-1,2-diamine ligands.   [2 marks]
    b)   Draw a diagram to show the bonding of one ethane-1,2-diamine ligand with Co^{2+}.   [2 marks]

Put your hands up — we've got you surrounded...

You never get transition metal ions floating round by themselves in a solution — they'll always be surrounded by other molecules. It's kind of like what'd happen if you put a dish of sweets in a room of eight (or eighteen) year-olds. When you're drawing complex ions, don't forget to include the dashed and wedge-shaped bonds to show that it's 3-D.

Formation of Coloured Ions

Transition metal complex ions have distinctive colours, which is handy when it comes to identifying them. This page explains why they're so colourful.

Ligands **Split** the 3d Subshell into **Two Energy Levels**

Normally the 3d orbitals of transition element ions **all** have the **same energy**. But when **ligands** come along and bond to the ions, some of the orbitals are given more energy than others. This splits the 3d orbitals into **two different energy levels**.

Electrons tend to **occupy the lower orbitals** (the ground state). To jump up to the higher orbitals (excited states) they need **energy** equal to the energy gap, ΔE. They get this energy from **visible light**.

The 3d orbitals of a Ni^{2+} ion without any ligands.

The 3d orbitals of $[Ni(H_2O)_6]^{2+}$

The energy **absorbed** when electrons jump up can be worked out using this formula:

$$\Delta E = h\nu$$

where ν = frequency of light absorbed (hertz/Hz) and h = Planck's constant (6.63×10^{-34} Js)

The amount of energy needed to make electrons jump depends upon the **central metal ion** and its **oxidation state**, the **ligands** and the **coordination number**, as these affect the **size of the energy gap**.

The **Colours** of Compounds are the **Complement** of Those That are Absorbed

When **visible light** hits a transition metal ion, some frequencies are **absorbed** when electrons jump up to the higher orbitals. The frequencies absorbed depend on the size of the **energy gap**.

The rest of the frequencies are **reflected**. These **reflected** frequencies combine to make the **complement** of the colour of the absorbed frequencies — this is the **colour** you see.

frequency increases ⟹

For example, $[Cu(H_2O)_6]^{2+}$ ions absorb **yellow light**. The remaining frequencies **combine** to produce the **complementary colour** — in this case that's blue. So $[Cu(H_2O)_6]^{2+}$ solution appears **blue**.

If there are **no** 3d electrons or the 3d subshell is **full**, then no electrons will jump, so **no energy** will be absorbed. If there's no energy absorbed, the compound will look **white** or **colourless**.

Transition Metal Ions can be Identified by their Colour

It'd be nice if each transition metal formed ions or complexes with just one colour, but sadly it's not that simple. The **colour of a complex** can be altered by any of the factors that can affect the size of the **energy gap**.

1) **Changes in oxidation state** — see page 86-87 for more examples.

Complex:	$[Fe(H_2O)_6]^{2+}_{(aq)}$	→	$[Fe(H_2O)_6]^{3+}_{(aq)}$		$[V(H_2O)_6]^{2+}_{(aq)}$	→	$[V(H_2O)_6]^{3+}_{(aq)}$
Oxidation state:	+2	→	+3	and	+2	→	+3
Colour:	pale green	→	yellow		violet	→	green

2) **Changes in coordination number** — this always involves a change of ligand too.

Complex:	$[Cu(H_2O)_6]^{2+} + 4Cl^-$	→	$[CuCl_4]^{2-} + 6H_2O$
Coordination number:	6	→	4
Colour:	blue	→	yellow

3) **Changes in ligand** — this can cause a colour change even if the oxidation state and coordination number remain the same.

Complex:	$[Co(H_2O)_6]^{2+} + 6NH_3$	→	$[Co(NH_3)_6]^{2+} + 6H_2O$
Oxidation state:	+2	→	+2
Colour:	pink	→	straw coloured

Formation of Coloured Ions

Spectrometry can be used to Find Concentrations of Transition Metal Ions

Spectrometry can be used to determine the **concentration of a solution** by measuring how much **light** it **absorbs**.

1) **White light** is shone through a **filter**, which is chosen to **only** let the **colour of light** through that is **absorbed** by the sample.

2) The light then passes through the sample to a **colorimeter**, which calculates **how much light** was **absorbed** by the sample.

3) The more **concentrated** a coloured solution is, the more light it will absorb. So you can use this measurement to work out the **concentration** of a solution of transition metal ions.

White light source   Filter   Sample of ion solution   Colorimeter

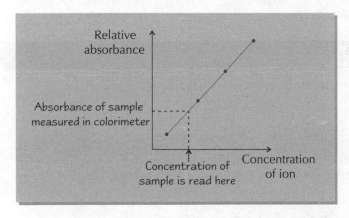

Before you can find the unknown concentration of a sample, you have to produce a **calibration graph** — like the lovely one on the left.

This involves measuring the **absorbances** of **known concentrations** of solutions and plotting the results on a graph.

Once you've done this, you can measure the absorbance of your sample and read its **concentration** off the graph.

Stanley's concentration was strong — he'd show this cowboy who's boss.

Practice Questions

Q1 Which subshell is split by the presence of ligands?

Q2 What **two** factors are changing in the following reaction that will cause a change in colour?

$$[Co(H_2O)_6]^{2+} + 4Cl^- \rightarrow [CoCl_4]^{2-} + 6H_2O$$

Q3 What does a colorimeter measure?

Q4 What is the purpose of the filter in spectrometry?

Exam Questions

1 a) Explain why complex transition metal ions such as $[Fe(H_2O)_6]^{2+}$ are coloured.   [2 marks]

   b) State three changes to a complex ion that would result in a change in colour.   [3 marks]

2 Colorimetry can be used to determine the concentration of a coloured solution. Briefly describe how you would construct a calibration graph, given a coloured solution of known concentration.   [3 marks]

3 The frequency of light absorbed by a transition metal complex ion can be determined from the equation $\Delta E = h\nu$.

   a) State what is meant by ΔE and what change this represents within the complex ion.   [2 marks]

   b) Using a noble gas core, [Ar], complete the electron arrangements for the following ions

     (i) Cu^+ [1 mark]

     (ii) Cu^{2+} [1 mark]

   c) Which one of the above ions has coloured compounds? State the feature of its electron arrangement that suggests this.   [2 marks]

Blue's not my complementary colour — it clashes with my hair...

Transition metal ions are pretty colours, don't you think? The Romans did — they used iron, copper, cobalt and manganese compounds to add colour to glass objects. I'm not sure that they knew the colours were affected by variable oxidation states, ligands and coordination number, but it's pretty impressive even so.

Variable Oxidation States

One of the reasons why transition metal complexes have such a big range of colours is their variable oxidation states.

Chromium Can Exist in the +2, +3 and +6 Oxidation States

Chromium most commonly exists in the **+3** or **+6** oxidation state.
It can exist in the +2 oxidation state as well, but it's much **less stable**.

In the +6 oxidation state, chromium can form chromate(VI) ions, CrO_4^{2-} **and** dichromate(VI) ions, $Cr_2O_7^{2-}$. Both these ions are good oxidising agents because they can easily be reduced to Cr^{3+}.

Oxidation state	Formula of ion	Colour of ion
+6	$Cr_2O_7^{2-}{}_{(aq)}$	Orange
+6	$CrO_4^{2-}{}_{(aq)}$	Yellow
+3	$Cr^{3+}{}_{(aq)}$	Green (Violet)
+2	$Cr^{2+}{}_{(aq)}$	Blue

When Cr^{3+} ions are surrounded by 6 water ligands they're violet. But the water ligands are often substituted, so this solution usually looks green instead.

Chromate(VI) Ions, CrO_4^{2-}, and Dichromate(VI) Ions, $Cr_2O_7^{2-}$, Exist in Equilibrium

1) When an **alkali** (OH^- ions) is added to aqueous **dichromate(VI) ions**, the orange colour turns **yellow**, because aqueous **chromate(VI) ions** form.

$$Cr_2O_7^{2-}{}_{(aq)} + OH^-{}_{(aq)} \rightarrow 2CrO_4^{2-}{}_{(aq)} + H^+{}_{(aq)}$$
orange   **yellow**

2) When an **acid** (H^+ ions) is added to aqueous **chromate(VI) ions**, the yellow colour turns **orange**, because aqueous **dichromate(VI) ions** form.

$$2CrO_4^{2-}{}_{(aq)} + H^+{}_{(aq)} \rightarrow Cr_2O_7^{2-}{}_{(aq)} + OH^-{}_{(aq)}$$
yellow   **orange**

3) These are **opposite processes** and the two ions exist in **equilibrium**.

$$Cr_2O_7^{2-}{}_{(aq)} + H_2O_{(l)} \rightleftharpoons 2CrO_4^{2-}{}_{(aq)} + 2H^+{}_{(aq)}$$

This isn't a redox process because chromium stays in the +6 oxidation state.

The **position** of equilibrium depends on the **pH** — yep, it's good ol' Le Chatelier's principle again.
If **H^+ ions** are added, the equilibrium shifts to the **left** so orange $Cr_2O_7^{2-}$ ions are formed.
If **OH^- ions** are added, H+ ions are **removed** and the equilibrium shifts to the **right**, forming **yellow CrO_4^{2-} ions**.

Chromium Ions can be Oxidised and Reduced

1) Dichromate(VI) ions can be **reduced** using a good reducing agent, such as **zinc and dilute acid**.

Oxidation states: +6   0   +2   +3
$$Cr_2O_7^{2-}{}_{(aq)} + 14H^+{}_{(aq)} + 3Zn_{(s)} \rightarrow 3Zn^{2+}{}_{(aq)} + 2Cr^{3+}{}_{(aq)} + 7H_2O_{(l)}$$
orange   **green**

2) Zinc will **reduce** Cr^{3+} further to Cr^{2+} —

$$2Cr^{3+}{}_{(aq)} + Zn_{(s)} \rightarrow Zn^{2+}{}_{(aq)} + 2Cr^{2+}{}_{(aq)}$$
green   **blue**

But unless you use an inert atmosphere, you're wasting your time — Cr^{2+} is so **unstable** that it oxidises straight back to Cr^{3+} in air.

3) You can oxidise Cr^{3+} to chromate(VI) ions with **hydrogen peroxide, H_2O_2,** in an **alkaline** solution.

Oxidation states: +3   +6
$$2Cr^{3+}{}_{(aq)} + 10OH^-{}_{(aq)} + 3H_2O_{2(aq)} \rightarrow 2CrO_4^{2-}{}_{(aq)} + 8H_2O_{(l)}$$
green   **yellow**

Here's a summary of all the chromium reactions you need to know:

$$Cr_2O_7^{2-}{}_{(aq)} \underset{OH^-{}_{(aq)}}{\overset{H^+{}_{(aq)}}{\rightleftharpoons}} CrO_4^{2-}{}_{(aq)}$$

REDUCTION $H^+{}_{(aq)}/Zn_{(s)}$

OXIDATION $OH^-{}_{(aq)}/H_2O_{2(aq)}$

$Cr^{3+}{}_{(aq)}$

REDUCTION $H^+{}_{(aq)}/Zn_{(s)}$ (inert atmosphere)

OXIDATION air

$Cr^{2+}{}_{(aq)}$

Variable Oxidation States

Cobalt Can Exist as Co²⁺ and Co³⁺

Cobalt can exist in two oxidation states — **+2** as **Co^{2+}**, and **+3** as **Co^{3+}**. It much prefers to be in the **+2** state though.

1) Co^{3+} can be made by oxidising $Co^{2+}_{(aq)}$ with **hydrogen peroxide** in alkaline conditions.

$$2Co^{2+}_{(aq)} + H_2O_{2(aq)} \rightarrow 2Co^{3+}_{(aq)} + 2OH^-_{(aq)}$$

2) You can also oxidise Co^{2+} with **air in an ammoniacal solution**. You place Co^{2+} ions in an excess of **aqueous ammonia**, which causes **$[Co(NH_3)_6]^{2+}$ ions** to form. If these complex ions are left to stand in **air**, **oxygen** oxidises them to **$[Co(NH_3)_6]^{3+}$**.

The reaction is done this way because $[Co(NH_3)_6]^{2+}_{(aq)}$ ions are far **easier to oxidise** than $[Co(H_2O)_6]^{2+}_{(aq)}$ ions.

Practice Questions

Q1 What colour change is seen when acid is added to aqueous chromate(VI) ions? Name the new chromium ion.

Q2 Name the two reagents needed to oxidise chromium(III) to chromium(VI).

Q3 Describe two ways of oxidising $Co^{2+}_{(aq)}$ to $Co^{3+}_{(aq)}$.

Q4 Show that the oxidation state of cobalt in $Co(OH)_2$ is +2.

Exam Questions

1   Acidified dichromate ions can act as powerful oxidising agents.

a)   Write a half-equation for the reduction of dichromate ions to chromium(III) ions in acid solution.   [1 mark]

b)   Ethanol is oxidised to ethanal by dichromate ions.

(i) Write a balanced equation for the oxidation of ethanol to ethanal by dichromate ions in acid solution.   [2 marks]

(ii) Give the colour change seen in this reaction.   [1 mark]

c) SO_2 gas is oxidised to SO_4^{2-} ions by acidified dichromate.

(i) Write a half-equation for the oxidation of SO_2 to SO_4^{2-}.   [1 mark]

(ii) Write an equation for the oxidation of SO_2 by acidified dichromate ions.   [1 mark]

2   The following reaction sequence involves complex ions of a transition element.
The ion is initially in its +3 oxidation state.

$$\begin{array}{ccc}
+ \text{ } H_2O_2 \text{ in} & & \\
\text{alkaline solution} & + \text{ acid} & \\
\end{array}$$

$$\mathbf{X} \xrightarrow{\hspace{2cm}} \mathbf{Y} \xrightarrow{\hspace{2cm}} \mathbf{Z}$$

green solution   yellow solution   solution

a)   Identify the transition metal ion responsible for the green solution **X**.   [1 mark]

b)   The half-equation for the hydrogen peroxide reaction is $H_2O_2 + 2e^- \rightarrow 2OH^-$.
Give the oxidation number of oxygen in hydrogen peroxide.   [1 mark]

c)   Addition of an acid to the yellow solution causes a further colour change that is **not** a redox reaction,
forming Z. Write an equation for this reaction and give the colour of the solution formed.   [2 marks]

My girlfriend is usually in the +6 or +8 aggravation states...

Sorry, I'm too tired to tell you anything meaningful right now, so you're on your own I'm afraid... I'm going to have a nap and probably have another dream where I'm being attacked by a wallaby the size of a house... ....
....

Titrations with Transition Metals

These titrations are redox titrations. They're like acid-base titrations, but different. You don't need an indicator for a start.

Titrations Using **Transition Element Ions** are **Redox** Titrations

Titrations using transition element ions let you find out how much **oxidising agent** is needed to **exactly** react with a quantity of **reducing agent**. If you know the **concentration** of either the oxidising agent or the reducing agent, you can use the titration results to work out the concentration of the other.

1) First you measure out a quantity of **reducing agent**, e.g. aqueous Fe^{2+} ions, using a pipette, and put it in a conical flask.

2) Using a **measuring cylinder**, you add about **20 cm³ of dilute sulfuric acid** to the flask — this is an excess, so you don't have to be too exact.

3) Now you add the **oxidising agent**, e.g. aqueous potassium manganate(VII), to the reducing agent using a **burette**, **swirling** the conical flask as you do so.

4) The **oxidising agent** that you add reacts with the reducing agent. This reaction will continue until **all** of the reducing agent is used up. The **very next drop** you add to the flask will give the mixture the **colour of the oxidising agent**. (You could use a coloured reducing agent and a colourless oxidising agent instead — then you'd be watching for the moment that the colour in the flask disappears.)

5) Stop when the mixture in the flask **just** becomes tainted with the colour of the oxidising agent (the **end point**) and record the volume of the oxidising agent added. This is the **rough titration**.

6) Now you do some **accurate titrations**. You need to do a few until you get **two or more** readings that are **within 0.10 cm³** of each other.

Burette

Oxidising agent

Reducing agent and dilute sulfuric acid

You can also do titrations the other way round — adding the reducing agent to the oxidising agent.

The two main **oxidising agents** used are:

1) **Manganate(VII) ions** (MnO_4^-) in **aqueous potassium manganate(VII)** ($KMnO_4$) — these are **purple**.

2) **Dichromate(VI) ions** ($Cr_2O_7^{2-}$) in **aqueous potassium dichromate(VI)** ($K_2Cr_2O_7$) — these are **orange**.

The **acid** is added to make sure there are plenty of **H^+ ions** to allow the oxidising agent to be reduced.

Use the **Titration Results** to **Calculate** the **Concentration** of a Reagent...

Example: 27.5 cm³ of 0.0200 moldm⁻³ aqueous potassium manganate(VII) reacted with 25.0 cm³ of acidified iron(II) sulfate solution. Calculate the concentration of Fe^{2+} ions in the solution.

$$MnO_4^-{}_{(aq)} + 8H^+{}_{(aq)} + 5Fe^{2+}{}_{(aq)} \rightarrow Mn^{2+}{}_{(aq)} + 4H_2O_{(l)} + 5Fe^{3+}{}_{(aq)}$$

1) Work out the number of **moles of MnO_4^- ions** added to the flask.

Number of moles MnO_4^- added $= \dfrac{\text{concentration} \times \text{volume}}{1000} = \dfrac{0.0200 \times 27.5}{1000} = 5.50 \times 10^{-4}$ moles

Manganate 007, licensed to oxidise.

2) Look at the balanced equation to find how many moles of **Fe^{2+}** react with **every mole** of MnO_4^-. Then you can work out the **number of moles of Fe^{2+}** in the flask.

5 moles of Fe^{2+} react with 1 mole of MnO_4^-. So moles of $Fe^{2+} = 5.50 \times 10^{-4} \times 5 = 2.75 \times 10^{-3}$ moles.

3) Work out the **number of moles of Fe^{2+}** that would be in 1000 cm³ (1 dm³) of solution — this is the **concentration**.

25.00 cm³ of solution contained 2.75×10^{-3} moles of Fe^{2+}.

1000 cm³ of solution would contain $\dfrac{(2.75 \times 10^{-3}) \times 1000}{25.0} = 0.11$ moles of Fe^{2+}.

So the concentration of Fe^{2+} is **0.11 moldm⁻³**.

Titrations with Transition Metals

...Or the *Volume* of a Reagent

Example: Aqueous potassium dichromate(VI) with a concentration of 0.008 moldm⁻³ was used to completely oxidise 25.0 cm³ of 0.06 moldm⁻³ acidified iron(II) sulfate solution. Calculate the volume of potassium dichromate(VI) solution used.

$$Cr_2O_7^{2-}{}_{(aq)} + 14H^+{}_{(aq)} + 6Fe^{2+}{}_{(aq)} \rightarrow 2Cr^{3+}{}_{(aq)} + 7H_2O_{(l)} + 6Fe^{3+}{}_{(aq)}$$

1) Work out the number of **moles of Fe²⁺ ions** in the flask to begin with.

$$\text{Number of moles Fe}^{2+} = \frac{\text{concentration} \times \text{volume}}{1000} = \frac{0.06 \times 25.0}{1000} = 1.5 \times 10^{-3} \text{ moles}$$

2) Look at the balanced equation to find how many moles of **Fe²⁺** react with **every mole** of $Cr_2O_7^{2-}$. Then you can work out the **number of moles of $Cr_2O_7^{2-}$** needed.

6 moles of Fe²⁺ react with 1 mole of $Cr_2O_7^{2-}$. So moles of $Cr_2O_7^{2-}$ = 1.5 × 10⁻³ ÷ 6 = 2.5 × 10⁻⁴ moles.

3) Rearrange the formula above to find the **volume** of **0.008 moldm⁻³** dichromate solution that contains **2.5 × 10⁻⁴ moles of $Cr_2O_7^{2-}$**.

$$\text{Volume of } Cr_2O_7^{2-} = \frac{\text{number of moles} \times 1000}{\text{concentration}} = \frac{(2.5 \times 10^{-4}) \times 1000}{0.008} = 31.25 \text{ cm}^3$$

Practice Questions

Q1 Why is an excess of acid added to potassium manganate(VII) titrations?

Q2 Outline how you would carry out a titration of Fe²⁺ with MnO_4^- in acid solution.

Q3 What colour marks the end-point of a redox titration when potassium manganate(VII) is added from the burette?

Q4 What colour is aqueous potassium dichromate?

Exam Questions

1 0.100 g of a sample of steel containing carbon and iron only was dissolved in sulfuric acid. The resulting solution was titrated using 29.40 cm³ of 0.0100 moldm⁻³ potassium dichromate(VI). The equation for the reaction is $Cr_2O_7^{2-} + 6Fe^{2+} + 14H^+ \rightarrow 2Cr^{3+} + 6Fe^{3+} + 7H_2O$

   a) Calculate the number of moles of dichromate ions added. [2 marks]

   b) How many moles of Fe²⁺ will have reacted? [1 mark]

   c) Calculate the mass of pure iron in the steel. [2 marks]

   d) Calculate the percentage of iron in the steel. [1 mark]

2 A sample of sodium ethanedioate is dissolved in dilute sulfuric acid. The solution is titrated using 18.30 cm³ of 0.0200 moldm⁻³ potassium manganate(VII).

   The equation for the reaction is: $2MnO_4^- + 5C_2O_4^{2-} + 16H^+ \rightarrow 2Mn^{2+} + 10CO_2 + 8H_2O$

   Calculate the mass of $Na_2C_2O_4$ in the initial sample. [7 marks]

3 A 0.1 moldm⁻³ solution of iron(II) sulfate has been partly oxidised by the air to an iron(III) compound. Explain how you could use a standard solution of potassium manganate(VII) to find the actual concentration of Fe²⁺ remaining. [4 marks]

And how many moles does it take to change a light bulb....

The example calculations on these two pages might look complicated, but if you break them down into a series of steps, they're really not that bad — especially as you've done titration calculations before. You know, with acids and bases? Back in Unit 4: Section 1? What do you mean you don't remember — go back and have another look.

Uses of Transition Metals

Transition metals aren't just good — they're grrrreat.

Transition Metal Catalysts *Work by* Changing Oxidation States

Transition metals and their compounds make good catalysts because they can **change oxidation states** by gaining or losing electrons within their **d orbitals**. This means they can **transfer electrons** to **speed up** reactions.

For example, in the **Contact Process**, vanadium(V) oxide is able to **oxidise SO₂ to SO₃** because it can be **reduced** to vanadium(IV) oxide. It's then **oxidised** back to vanadium(V) oxide by oxygen ready to start all over again.

This example uses a heterogeneous catalyst (see below), but the principle also applies to homogeneous catalysts.

Vanadium oxidises SO₂ to SO₃ and is reduced itself.

$$\overset{+5}{V_2O_5} + SO_2 \rightarrow \overset{+4}{V_2O_4} + SO_3$$

vanadium(V) → vanadium(IV)

The reduced catalyst is then oxidised by oxygen gas back to its original state.

$$\overset{+4}{V_2O_4} + \tfrac{1}{2}O_2 \rightarrow \overset{+5}{V_2O_5}$$

vanadium(IV) → vanadium(V)

Heterogeneous Catalysts *are in a* Different Phase *From the* Reactants

A heterogeneous catalyst is one that is in a **different phase** from the reactants — i.e. in a different **physical state**. For example, in the Haber Process (see below) **gases** are passed over a **solid iron catalyst**.

The **reaction** happens on the **surface** of the **heterogeneous catalyst**. So, **increasing** the **surface area** of the catalyst increases the number of molecules that can **react** at the same time, **increasing the rate** of the reaction.

Support mediums are often used to make the **area** of a catalyst **as large as possible**. For example, **catalytic converters** (which 'clean up' emissions from car engines) contain a **ceramic lattice** coated with a thin layer of **rhodium**. The **rhodium** acts as a **catalyst** helping to convert the **really nasty waste gases** to less harmful products.

$$2CO_{(g)} + 2NO_{(g)} \xrightarrow{\text{Rh}_{(s)}\text{ catalyst}} 2CO_{2(g)} + N_{2(g)}$$

The lattice structure **maximises the surface area** of the catalyst, making it more effective. And, it **minimises the cost** of the catalyst because only a **thin coating** is needed.

Examples of **heterogeneous catalysts** include:

You need to know these examples of heterogeneous catalysts.

1) **Iron** in the **Haber Process** for making **ammonia**: $N_{2(g)} + 3H_{2(g)} \xrightarrow{\text{Fe}_{(s)}\text{ catalyst}} 2NH_{3(g)}$

2) **Vanadium(V) oxide** in the **Contact Process** for making **sulfuric acid**: $SO_{2(g)} + \tfrac{1}{2}O_{2(g)} \xrightarrow{\text{V}_2\text{O}_{5(s)}\text{ catalyst}} SO_{3(g)}$

3) **Chromium(III) oxide** in the manufacture of **methanol from CO**: $CO_{(g)} + 2H_{2(g)} \xrightarrow{\text{Cr}_2\text{O}_{3(s)}\text{ catalyst}} CH_3OH_{(g)}$

Impurities *Can* Poison Heterogeneous Catalysts

1) During a reaction, reactants are **adsorbed** onto active sites on the **surfaces** of **heterogeneous catalysts**.

2) **Impurities** in the reaction mixture may also **bind** to the catalyst's surface and **block reactants** from being adsorbed. This process is called **catalyst poisoning**.

3) Catalyst poisoning **reduces the surface area** of the catalyst available to the reactants, **slowing down the reaction**.

4) Catalyst poisoning **increases the cost** of a chemical process because **less product** can be made in a certain **time** or with a certain amount of **energy**. The **catalyst** may even need **replacing or regenerating**, which also costs money.

Examples of catalyst poisoning include:

1) **Lead** poisons the catalyst in **catalytic converters**:
    Catalytic converters **reduce harmful emissions** from car engines. **Lead** can **coat the surface** of the catalyst in a catalytic converter, so vehicles that have them fitted must only be run on **unleaded petrol**.

2) **Sulfur** poisons the iron catalyst in the **Haber Process**:
    The **hydrogen** in the Haber process is produced from **methane**. The methane is obtained from natural gas, which contains impurities, including **sulfur** compounds. Any sulfur that is not removed is **adsorbed** onto the iron, forming iron sulfide, and stopping the iron from catalysing the reaction efficiently.

Uses of Transition Metals

Homogeneous Catalysts are in the Same Phase as the Reactants

Homogeneous catalysts are in the **same physical state** as the reactants.
Usually a **homogeneous** catalyst is an **aqueous catalyst** for a reaction between two **aqueous solutions**.

A homogeneous catalyst works by forming an **intermediate species**.
The **reactants** combine with the **catalyst** to make an **intermediate species**,
which then reacts to form the **products** and **reform the catalyst**.

This causes the enthalpy profile for a **homogeneously catalysed**
reaction to have **two humps** in it, corresponding to the two reactions.

The activation energy needed to form the **intermediates** (and to form the
products from the intermediates) is **lower** than that needed to make the
products directly from the reactants.

The catalyst is always **reformed** so it can carry on catalysing the reaction.

Fe²⁺ Catalyses the Reaction Between S₂O₈²⁻ and I⁻

The **redox** reaction between iodide ions and peroxodisulfate ($S_2O_8^{2-}$) ions takes place **annoyingly slowly**
because both ions are **negatively charged**. The ions **repel** each other, so it's unlikely they'll **collide** and **react**.

$$S_2O_8^{2-}{}_{(aq)} + 2I^-{}_{(aq)} \rightarrow I_{2(aq)} + 2SO_4^{2-}{}_{(aq)}$$

But if **Fe²⁺ ions** are added, things are really **speeded up** because each stage of
the reaction involves a **positive and a negative ion**, so there's **no repulsion**.
First, the Fe²⁺ ions are **oxidised** to Fe³⁺ ions by the $S_2O_8^{2-}$ ions.

The newly formed intermediate Fe³⁺ ions
now **easily oxidise** the I⁻ ions to iodine,
and the **catalyst is regenerated**.

The negative charges of the two ions is one reason why this reaction has high activation energy.

$$S_2O_8^{2-}{}_{(aq)} + 2Fe^{2+}{}_{(aq)} \rightarrow 2Fe^{3+}{}_{(aq)} + 2SO_4^{2-}{}_{(aq)}$$

$$2Fe^{3+}{}_{(aq)} + 2I^-{}_{(aq)} \rightarrow I_{2(aq)} + 2Fe^{2+}{}_{(aq)}$$

Fe²⁺ is in the same phase as the reactants, so it's a homogeneous catalyst.

You can test for **iodine** by adding **starch solution** — it'll turn **blue-black** if iodine is present.

Autocatalysis is when a Product Catalyses the Reaction

Another example of a **homogeneous catalyst** is Mn²⁺ in the reaction between $C_2O_4^{2-}$ and MnO_4^-.
It's an **autocatalysis reaction** because Mn²⁺ is a **product** of the reaction and **acts as a catalyst** for the reaction.
This means that as the reaction progresses and the **amount** of the **product increases**, the reaction **speeds up**.

$$2MnO_4^-{}_{(aq)} + 16H^+{}_{(aq)} + 5C_2O_4^{2-}{}_{(aq)} \rightarrow 2Mn^{2+}{}_{(aq)} + 8H_2O_{(l)} + 10CO_{2(g)}$$

Transition metals make good catalysts, but that isn't their only use — it's time to look at some other places they turn up.

Fe²⁺ in Haemoglobin Allows Oxygen to be Carried in the Blood

The blood product, **haemoglobin**, is a complex formed from **Fe²⁺ ions** (see page 83 for the structure). Both **water** and
oxygen will bind to the Fe²⁺ ion as **ligands**, so the complex can **transport oxygen** to where it's needed, and then swap
it for a water molecule — here's **how it works**.

1) In the lungs, where the oxygen concentration is high, the water ligand is **substituted** for an **oxygen molecule**
   to form **oxyhaemoglobin**, which is carried **around the body** in the blood.

2) When the **oxyhaemoglobin** gets to a place where oxygen is needed, the **oxygen molecule** is **exchanged** for a
   water molecule. The haemoglobin then **returns to the lungs** and the whole process starts again.

This process can be disrupted if **carbon monoxide** is inhaled. The **haemoglobin** swaps its **water** ligand for a **carbon
monoxide** ligand, forming **carboxyhaemoglobin**. This is bad news because carbon monoxide is a **strong** ligand and
doesn't readily exchange with oxygen or water ligands, meaning the haemoglobin **can't transport oxygen** any more.
Carbon monoxide poisoning starves the organs of oxygen — it can cause **headaches**, **dizziness**, **unconsciousness** and
even **death** if it's not treated.

Uses of Transition Metals

Cisplatin *is an* Anti-Cancer Drug

Cisplatin is a complex of platinum(II) with two chloride ions and two ammonia molecules in a square planar shape.

Note that the two Cl⁻ ions are **next to each other**, never opposite, as this would be a different isomer (transplatin) with different biological properties.

Cisplatin is **active against a variety of cancers**, including lung and bladder cancer because it **prevents cancer cells from reproducing**.

The downside is that cisplatin also prevents normal cells from reproducing, including blood and hair cells. This can cause **hair loss** and **suppress the immune system**, increasing the risk of infection. Cisplatin may also cause **damage to the kidneys**.

Tollens' Reagent *Contains a Silver Complex*

Tollens' reagent is prepared by adding just enough ammonia solution to silver nitrate solution to form a colourless solution containing the complex ion $[Ag(NH_3)_2]^+$.

Tollens' reagent is used to distinguish between **aldehydes** and **ketones** — aldehydes react to give a **silver mirror** on the inside of the test tube.

$$RCHO + 2[Ag(NH_3)_2]^+ + 3OH^- \rightarrow RCOO^- + 2Ag + 4NH_3 + 2H_2O$$

Ketones don't react with Tollens' reagent.

Steve was seeking professional help about his silver complex.

Practice Questions

Q1 What property of transition elements makes them good catalysts?

Q2 Which catalyst is used in the manufacture of methanol from carbon monoxide?

Q3 What term describes the process when a product catalyses a reaction?

Q4 State a medical use of the Pt(II) complex cisplatin.

Exam Questions

1   a)   Using equations, explain how vanadium(V) oxide acts as a catalyst in the Contact Process.   [4 marks]
    b)   (i)   Describe how heterogeneous catalysts can become poisoned and give an example.   [3 marks]
         (ii) What are the consequences of catalytic poisoning?   [2 marks]

2   a)   Explain the difference between homogeneous and heterogeneous catalysts.   [2 marks]
    b)   H⁺ ions are used to catalyse the reaction between $C_2H_5OH_{(aq)}$ and $CH_3COOH_{(aq)}$.
         (i)   What type of catalysis is this?   [1 mark]
         (ii) Sketch an enthalpy profile diagram for this reaction to show the catalysed and uncatalysed routes
               for this exothermic reaction.   [3 marks]

3   Tollens' reagent contains a transition metal complex ion.
    a)   Which two types of organic compound is Tollens' reagent used to distinguish between?   [1 mark]
    b)   What is seen when a positive reaction occurs with Tollens' reagent?   [1 mark]
    c)   Give the:
         (i) formula   (ii) shape   (iii) colour
         of the transition metal complex ion in Tollens' reagent.   [3 marks]

Bagpuss, Sylvester, Tom — *the top three on my catalyst...*

Hopefully you'll have realised from these last three pages that transition metals are really quite useful. You should also know the difference between heterogeneous and homogeneous catalysts and why the variable oxidation states of transition metals make them good catalysts. If you do, then go grab yourself a cup of tea— it speeds up the rate of revision, you know.

Metal-Aqua Ions

Remember all the stuff on pages 82-85 about complex ions and their pretty coloured solutions?
Well this section's all about their reactions. So prepare yourself for more colour changes than a chameleon playing twister...

Metal Ions Become Hydrated in Water

When **transition metal compounds** dissolve in water, the water molecules form **coordinate bonds** with the **metal ions**. This forms **metal-aqua complex ions**. In general, **six water molecules** form coordinate bonds with each metal ion.

The water molecules do this by donating a **non-bonding pair of electrons** from their oxygen.

The diagrams show the metal-aqua ions formed by **iron** — $Fe(H_2O)_6^{2+}$ and by **chromium** — $Cr(H_2O)_6^{3+}$.

This is the charge on the metal ion (water molecules are neutral).

A Lewis Acid Accepts Electrons — A Lewis Base Donates Electrons

The Brønsted-Lowry theory of acids and bases says that an **acid** is a **proton donor**, and a **base** is a **proton acceptor**.

$$NH_{3(aq)} + HCl_{(aq)} \rightarrow NH_4^+{}_{(aq)} + Cl^-{}_{(aq)}$$

HCl is donating a proton, so it's acting as a **Brønsted-Lowry acid**.
NH_3 is accepting a proton, so it's acting as a **Brønsted-Lowry base**.

Now look at the reaction that happens between **ammonia** and **boron trifluoride**:

$$NH_{3(aq)} + BF_{3(aq)} \rightarrow NH_3BF_{3(aq)}$$

This **doesn't** involve transferring protons, so it doesn't fit in with the Brønsted-Lowry acid-base theory. You'd think this would mean that it's not an acid-base reaction, but a chemist (Mr Lewis) came up with an alternative theory that broadens the definition of acids and bases. The Lewis theory is based on the transfer of **electrons**, rather than protons:

> A **Lewis acid** is an **electron pair acceptor**.
> A **Lewis base** is an **electron pair donor**.

In the reaction above, the **ammonia** molecule **donates** a pair of electrons to the boron atom, forming a **coordinate bond**.

$$H_3N\boldsymbol{:}\rightarrow BF_3$$

So **NH₃** is acting as a **Lewis base**, and **BF₃** is acting as a **Lewis acid**.

Some substances fit both the Brønsted-Lowry and the Lewis definitions of an acid or base. Others only fit one. So, if you're describing something as an acid or base, you should say whether it's a **Brønsted-Lowry** or a **Lewis** acid or base.

You Need to be Able to Spot Lewis Acids and Bases

Have a look at these examples:

$$H_2O + H^+ \rightarrow H_3O^+$$

Coordinate bond

The water molecule's donating an electron pair to the hydrogen ion, and the hydrogen ion is accepting an electron pair from the water. So the water molecule is the Lewis base and the hydrogen ion's the Lewis acid.

$$AlCl_3 + Cl^- \rightarrow AlCl_4^-$$

Coordinate bond

The aluminium chloride is accepting an electron pair — so it's the Lewis acid. The chloride ion is donating an electron pair — so it's the Lewis base.

Coordinate bonds always involve one substance donating an electron pair to another. So if there's a coordinate bond, there are no two ways about it — it **must** have been formed in a **Lewis acid-base reaction**.

They're **not** Brønsted-Lowry acids because they can't donate a proton (H⁺).

Metal ions act as **Lewis acids** in aqueous solution because they **accept electron pairs** from the water molecules that surround them. And the water molecules, like any **ligands**, are **electron pair donors** so they must be **Lewis bases**.

Metal-Aqua Ions

Solutions Containing Metal-Aqua Ions are Acidic

In a solution containing metal-aqua **2+** ions, there's a reaction between the metal-aqua ion and the water — this is a **hydrolysis** or **acidity reaction**.

E.g. $$Fe(H_2O)_6{}^{2+}{}_{(aq)} + H_2O_{(l)} \rightleftharpoons [Fe(H_2O)_5(OH)]^+{}_{(aq)} + H_3O^+{}_{(aq)}$$

Aqua-ironing —
it keeps those
flat fish smooth.

The metal-aqua **2+** ions release H^+ ions, so an **acidic** solution is formed.
There's only **slight** dissociation though, so the solution is only **weakly acidic**.

Metal-aqua **3+** ions react in the same way. They form **more acidic** solutions though.

E.g. $$Al(H_2O)_6{}^{3+}{}_{(aq)} + H_2O_{(l)} \rightleftharpoons [Al(H_2O)_5(OH)]^{2+}{}_{(aq)} + H_3O^+{}_{(aq)}$$

> In these forward reactions, the **metal-aqua ion** is acting as a **Brønsted-Lowry acid**. It **donates a proton** from one of its water ligands to a free water molecule.

> **Here's why 3+ metal-aqua ions form more acidic solutions than 2+ metal-aqua ions:**
>
> Metal 3+ ions are pretty **small** but have a **big charge** — so they've got a **high charge density** (otherwise known as **charge/size ratio**). The metal 2+ ions have a **much lower** charge density.
>
> This makes the 3+ ions much more **polarising** than the 2+ ions. More polarising power means that they attract **electrons** from the oxygen atoms of the coordinated water molecules more strongly, weakening the O–H bond.
>
> So it's more likely that a **hydrogen ion** will be released. And more hydrogen ions means a **more acidic** solution.

You Can Hydrolyse Metal-Aqua Ions Further to Form Precipitates

Adding **OH⁻ ions** to solutions of **metal-aqua ions** produces **insoluble metal hydroxides**.
Here's why:

↗ M might be Fe, Al or Cr.

1) In water, **metal-aqua 3+ ions** form the equilibrium: $M(H_2O)_6{}^{3+}{}_{(aq)} + H_2O_{(l)} \rightleftharpoons [M(H_2O)_5(OH)]^{2+}{}_{(aq)} + H_3O^+{}_{(aq)}$.
   If you add **OH⁻ ions** to the equilibrium H_3O^+ ions are removed — this shifts the equilibrium to the **right**.

2) Now another equilibrium is set up in the solution: $[M(H_2O)_5(OH)]^{2+}{}_{(aq)} + H_2O_{(l)} \rightleftharpoons [M(H_2O)_4(OH)_2]^+{}_{(aq)} + H_3O^+{}_{(aq)}$.
   Again the OH⁻ ions remove H_3O^+ ions from the solution, pulling the equilibrium to the right.

3) This happens one last time — now you're left with an **insoluble uncharged metal hydroxide**:
   $[M(H_2O)_4(OH)_2]^+{}_{(aq)} + H_2O_{(l)} \rightleftharpoons M(H_2O)_3(OH)_{3(s)} + H_3O^+{}_{(aq)}$.

The same thing happens with **metal-aqua 2+ ions** (e.g. Fe, Co or Cu), except this time there are only **two** steps:
$$M(H_2O)_6{}^{2+}{}_{(aq)} + H_2O_{(l)} \rightleftharpoons [M(H_2O)_5(OH)]^+{}_{(aq)} + H_3O^+{}_{(aq)} \longrightarrow [M(H_2O)_5(OH)]^+{}_{(aq)} + H_2O_{(l)} \rightleftharpoons M(H_2O)_4(OH)_{2(s)} + H_3O^+{}_{(aq)}$$

All the metal hydroxide precipitates **will dissolve in acid**. They act as Brønsted-Lowry bases and **accept H⁺ ions**. This **reverses** the hydrolysis reactions above.

Some metal hydroxides are **amphoteric** — they can act as both acids and bases. This means they'll **dissolve in an excess of base** as well as in **acids**. **Aluminium hydroxide** and **chromium(III) hydroxide** are **amphoteric**. They act as **Brønsted-Lowry acids** and **donate H⁺ ions** to the OH⁻ ions, forming **soluble compounds**.

$$Al(H_2O)_3(OH)_{3(s)} + OH^-{}_{(aq)} \rightleftharpoons [Al(H_2O)_2(OH)_4]^-{}_{(aq)} + H_2O_{(l)} \qquad Cr(OH)_3(H_2O)_{3(s)} + 3OH^-{}_{(aq)} \rightleftharpoons [Cr(OH)_6]^{3-}{}_{(aq)} + 3H_2O_{(l)}$$

Precipitates Form with Ammonia Solution...

The obvious way of adding hydroxide ions is to use a strong alkali, like **sodium hydroxide solution** — but you can use **ammonia solution** too. When ammonia dissolves in water this equilibrium occurs: $NH_3 + H_2O \rightleftharpoons NH_4^+ + OH^-$
Because hydroxide ions are formed, adding a **small** amount of ammonia solution gives the same results as sodium hydroxide.

In some cases, a further reaction happens if you add an **excess** of ammonia solution — the H_2O and OH⁻ ligands are displaced by NH_3 ligands. Have a look at the table on the next page to see which complexes this applies to.

...and Sodium Carbonate Too

Metal 2+ ions react with **sodium carbonate** to form **insoluble metal carbonates**, like this: → $$M(H_2O)_6{}^{2+}{}_{(aq)} + CO_3{}^{2-}{}_{(aq)} \rightleftharpoons MCO_{3(s)} + 6H_2O_{(l)}$$

But, **metal 3+ ions** are stronger acids so they always form **hydroxide precipitates** when you add sodium carbonate. The **carbonate ions** react with the H_3O^+ ions, removing them from the solution just like OH⁻ ions do.

> So you only get MCO_3 formed, not $M_2(CO_3)_3$.

Metal-Aqua Ions

Learn the **Colours** of All the **Complex Ion Solutions** and **Precipitates**

This handy table summarises all the compounds that are formed in the reactions on these pages.
You need to know the formulas of all the complex ions, and their colours.

Metal-aqua ion	With OH⁻$_{(aq)}$ or NH$_{3(aq)}$	With excess OH⁻$_{(aq)}$	With excess NH$_{3(aq)}$	With Na$_2$CO$_{3(aq)}$
$[Co(H_2O)_6]^{2+}$ pink solution	$Co(H_2O)_4(OH)_2$ blue-green precipitate	no change	$[Co(NH_3)_6]^{2+}$ straw coloured solution	$CoCO_3$ pink precipitate
$[Cu(H_2O)_6]^{2+}$ blue solution	$Cu(H_2O)_4(OH)_2$ blue precipitate	no change	$[Cu(NH_3)_4(H_2O)_2]^{2+}$ deep blue solution	$CuCO_3$ green-blue precipitate
$[Fe(H_2O)_6]^{2+}$ green solution	$Fe(H_2O)_4(OH)_2$ green precipitate	no change	no change	$FeCO_3$ green precipitate
$[Al(H_2O)_6]^{3+}$ colourless solution	$Al(H_2O)_3(OH)_3$ white precipitate	$[Al(H_2O)_2(OH)_4]^-$ colourless solution	no change	$Al(H_2O)_3(OH)_3$ white precipitate
$[Cr(H_2O)_6]^{3+}$ violet solution	$Cr(H_2O)_3(OH)_3$ green precipitate	$[Cr(OH)_6]^{3-}$ green solution	$[Cr(NH_3)_6]^{3+}$ purple solution	$Cr(H_2O)_3(OH)_3$ green precipitate
$[Fe(H_2O)_6]^{3+}$ yellow solution	$Fe(H_2O)_3(OH)_3$ brown precipitate	no change	no change	$Fe(H_2O)_3(OH)_3$ brown precipitate

Practice Questions

Q1 Explain why AlCl$_3$ can act as a Lewis acid.

Q2 Show by equations how Al(OH)$_3$ can act as both a Brønsted-Lowry acid and a Brønsted-Lowry base.

Q3 Explain why 3+ metal-aqua ions form more acidic solutions than 2+ metal-aqua ions.

Q4 What colour solution is formed when you add excess ammonia to a solution containing $[Co(H_2O)_6]^{2+}$ ions?

Exam Questions

1 Explain why separate solutions of iron(II) sulfate and iron(III) sulfate with equal concentrations
have different pH values. [4 marks]

2 Describe what you would see when ammonia solution is added slowly to a solution containing
copper(II) sulfate until it is in excess. Write equations for each reaction that occurs. [8 marks]

3 Aqueous ammonia was added to an aqueous solution of chromium(III) sulfate.
 a) Identify the chromium complex ion present in:
  (i) the aqueous chromium(III) sulfate. [1 mark]
  (ii) the green precipitate initially formed when aqueous ammonia is added. [1 mark]
  (iii) the purple solution when an excess of aqueous ammonia is added. [1 mark]
 b) Write an equation for the reaction in which the purple solution is formed from the green precipitate. [1 mark]

4 a) Describe what you would observe when aqueous sodium carbonate is added to:
  (i) aqueous iron(III) chloride. [1 mark]
  (ii) freshly-prepared aqueous iron(II) sulfate. [1 mark]
 b) Write an equation for the reaction of the iron(II)-aqua ion with the carbonate ion. [1 mark]
 c) If iron(II) sulfate solution is left to stand overnight in an open beaker before the aqueous sodium carbonate
  is added, then a different reaction is observed.
  (i) Describe the new observation. [1 mark]
  (ii) Explain this change. [1 mark]

Test-tube reactions — proper chemistry at last...

So many pretty colours. The only downside is that you have to remember them. But examiners do love to ask questions about colours of solutions and precipitates. So learn them all, or come exam day you'll end up feeling blue. Or possibly blue-green...

Substitution Reactions

There are more equations on this page than the number of elephants you can fit in a Mini.

Ligands can Change Places with One Another

One ligand can be **swapped** for another ligand — this is **ligand exchange**. It pretty much always causes a **colour change**.

1) If the ligands are of **similar size**, e.g. H_2O and NH_3, then the **coordination number** of the complex ion doesn't change, and neither does the **shape**.

$$[Co(H_2O)_6]^{2+}_{(aq)} + 6NH_{3(aq)} \rightarrow [Co(NH_3)_6]^{2+}_{(aq)} + 6H_2O_{(l)}$$
octahedral   octahedral
pink   straw coloured

$$[Cr(H_2O)_6]^{3+}_{(aq)} + 6OH^-_{(aq)} \rightarrow [Cr(OH)_6]^{3-}_{(aq)} + 6H_2O_{(l)}$$
octahedral   octahedral
violet   green

2) If the ligands are **different sizes**, e.g. H_2O and Cl^-, there's a **change of coordination number** and a **change of shape**.

$$[Cu(H_2O)_6]^{2+}_{(aq)} + 4Cl^-_{(aq)} \rightleftharpoons [CuCl_4]^{2-}_{(aq)} + 6H_2O_{(l)}$$
octahedral   tetrahedral
pale blue   yellow

$$[Co(H_2O)_6]^{2+}_{(aq)} + 4Cl^-_{(aq)} \rightleftharpoons [CoCl_4]^{2-}_{(aq)} + 6H_2O_{(l)}$$
octahedral   tetrahedral
pink   blue

> The forward reaction is endothermic, so the equilibrium can be shifted to the right-hand side by heating. The equilibrium will also shift to the right if you add more concentrated hydrochloric acid. Adding water to this equilibrium shifts it back to the left.

3) Sometimes the substitution is only **partial**.

$$[Cu(H_2O)_6]^{2+}_{(aq)} + 4NH_{3(aq)} \rightarrow [Cu(NH_3)_4(H_2O)_2]^{2+}_{(aq)} + 4H_2O_{(l)}$$
octahedral   elongated octahedral
pale blue   deep blue

$$[Fe(H_2O)_6]^{3+}_{(aq)} + SCN^-_{(aq)} \rightarrow [Fe(H_2O)_5SCN]^{2+}_{(aq)} + H_2O_{(l)}$$
octahedral   distorted octahedral
pale violet when pure   blood red

but this usually
looks **yellow** ⟶

Have a quick peek back at the reactions on page 94 — these were **ligand exchange reactions** too. In these, **hydroxide precipitates** were formed when a little bit of **sodium hydroxide** or **ammonia solution** was added to metal-aqua ions. The hydroxide precipitates sometimes **dissolved** when excess sodium hydroxide or ammonia solution was added.

Some Ligands Can Attach to the Metal Atom in More Than One Place

So far all the ligands in this section have been **unidentate**, but you'll remember from page 83 that ligands can also be **bidentate** or **multidentate**. Here's a quick recap of what that means:

1) **Unidentate** ligands have **one lone pair** of electrons to donate to the metal ion to form a **dative covalent bond**.

2) **Bidentate** ligands have **two lone pairs** of electrons to donate.

3) **Multidentate** ligands donate **more than one lone pair** of electrons to form **more than one coordinate bond** with the metal ion.

Polydent ate my hamster.

Different Ligands Form Different Strength Bonds

Ligand exchange reactions can be easily **reversed**, **UNLESS** the new complex ion is much **more stable** than the old one.

1) If the new ligands form **stronger** bonds with the central metal ion than the old ligands did, the change is **less easy** to reverse. E.g. **CN⁻ ions** form stronger coordinate bonds with Fe^{3+} ions than H_2O molecules did, so it's hard to reverse this reaction:

$$[Fe(H_2O)_6]^{3+}_{(aq)} + 6CN^-_{(aq)} \rightarrow [Fe(CN)_6]^{3-}_{(aq)} + 6H_2O_{(l)}$$

2) **Multidentate** ligands form more stable complexes than unidentate ligands, so a change like the one below is hard to reverse:

$$[Cu(H_2O)_6]^{2+}_{(aq)} + 3NH_2CH_2CH_2NH_{2(aq)} \rightarrow [Cu(NH_2CH_2CH_2NH_2)_3]^{2+}_{(aq)} + 6H_2O_{(l)}$$

This is explained on the next page...

Substitution Reactions

A *Positive Entropy Change* Makes a *More Stable Complex*

When a **ligand exchange reaction** occurs, bonds are **broken** and **formed**.
The **strength** of the bonds being broken is often very similar to the strength of the new bonds being made.
So the **enthalpy change** for a ligand exchange reaction is usually very **small**.

> **Example:** Substituting ammonia with ethane-1,2-diamine in a nickel complex:
>
> $[Ni(NH_3)_6]^{2+} + 3NH_2CH_2CH_2NH_2 \rightarrow [Ni(NH_2CH_2CH_2NH_2)_3]^{2+} + 6NH_3$ $\Delta H = -13$ kJmol^{-1}
>
> Break 6 coordinate bonds between Ni and N   Form 6 coordinate bonds between Ni and N

This is actually a **reversible** reaction, but the equilibrium lies so **far to the right** that it is thought of as being irreversible. $[Ni(NH_2CH_2CH_2NH_2)_3]^{2+}$ is **much more stable** than $[Ni(NH_3)_6]^{2+}$. This isn't accounted for by an enthalpy change, but an **increase in entropy** explains it:

> When unidentate ligands are substituted with bidentate or multidentate ligands, the number of particles increases — the **more particles**, the **greater the entropy**. Reactions that result in an increase in entropy are **more likely** to occur. This is known as the **chelate effect**.

In the reaction above the number of particles increased from 4 to 7.

So that's why multidentate ligands always form much more stable complexes than unidentate ligands.

When the **hexadentate ligand EDTA^{4-}** replaces unidentate or bidentate ligands, the complex formed is **loads more stable**.

> $[Cr(NH_3)_6]^{3+} + EDTA^{4-} \rightarrow [Cr(EDTA)]^- + 6NH_3$ **2 particles → 7 particles**
>
> $[Cr(NH_2CH_2CH_2NH_2)_3]^{3+} + EDTA^{4-} \rightarrow [Cr(EDTA)]^- + 3NH_2CH_2CH_2NH_2$ **2 particles → 4 particles**

It's difficult to reverse these reactions, because reversing them would cause a **decrease in entropy**.

Practice Questions

Q1 What colour is a solution of the complex ion $[Cu(NH_3)_4(H_2O)_2]^{2+}$?

Q2 What is the chelate effect?

Q3 When you add hydroxide ions to $[Cu(H_2O)_6]^{2+}$ you get a precipitate of $Cu(H_2O)_4(OH)_2$.
Adding extra H_2O does not reverse the reaction. Which ligand bonds more strongly to Cu^{2+}, OH^- or H_2O?

Exam Questions

1 An aqueous solution of copper sulfate contains the complex ion $[Cu(H_2O)_6]^{2+}$.
a) Write an equation for a ligand substitution reaction between $[Cu(H_2O)_6]^{2+}$ and chloride ions, in which all of the water ligands are replaced. Give the colour of the new complex formed. [3 marks]
b) The ethanedioate ion, $C_2O_4^{2-}$, is a bidentate ligand. Write an equation for a ligand substitution reaction between $[Cu(H_2O)_6]^{2+}$ and ethanedioate ions in which all of the water ligands are substituted. [2 marks]
c) $[Cu(H_2O)_6]^{2+}$ ions react with sodium hydroxide to form a precipitate. State the formula and colour of the complex ion contained in the precipitate. [2 marks]

You might need to check back to page 95 for some of these questions.

2 When a solution of EDTA^{4-} ions is added to an aqueous solution of $[Fe(H_2O)_6]^{3+}$ ions, a ligand substitution reaction occurs.
a) Write an equation for the reaction that takes place. [2 marks]
b) The new complex that is formed is more stable than $[Fe(H_2O)_6]^{3+}$. Explain why. [2 marks]
c) Another sample of $[Fe(H_2O)_6]^{3+}$ solution is mixed with a weak solution of sodium hydroxide. A brown precipitate forms. Give the formula of the complex ion contained in the precipitate. [1 mark]

3 A scientist takes three samples of a solution that contains the complex ion $[Co(H_2O)_6]^{2+}$. She mixes the first sample with a solution of chloride ions, the second with an excess of ammonia solution, and the third with a solution containing ethane-1,2-diamine. She observes the reactions that occur. Write an equation for a reaction the scientist observed where:
a) there was no change in the number of ligands surrounding the cobalt ion. [2 marks]
b) the number of ligands surrounding the cobalt ion changed, but the overall charge on the complex ion did not. [2 marks]
c) both the number of ligands surrounding the cobalt ion and the overall charge on the complex ion changed. [2 marks]

Ligand exchange — the musical chairs of the molecular world...

Ligands generally don't mind swapping with other ligands, so long as they're not too tightly attached to the central metal ion. They also won't fancy changing if it means forming fewer molecules and having less entropy. It's kind of like you wouldn't want to swap a cow for a handful of beans. Unless, of course, they're magic beans. But that almost never happens...

Practical and Investigative Skills

Don't Get **Carried Away** When Drawing Conclusions

The **data** should always **support** the conclusion. This may sound obvious but it's easy to **jump** to conclusions. Conclusions have to be **specific** — not make sweeping generalisations.

> **Example**
>
> The rate of an enzyme-controlled reaction was measured at **10 °C, 20 °C, 30 °C, 40 °C, 50 °C and 60 °C**. All other variables were kept constant, and the results are shown in this graph.
>
> A science magazine **concluded** from this data that enzyme X works best at **40 °C**. The data **doesn't** support this.
>
> The enzyme **could** work best at 42 °C or 47 °C but you can't tell from the data because **increases** of **10 °C** at a time were used. The rate of reaction at in-between temperatures **wasn't** measured.
>
> All you know is that it's faster at **40 °C** than at any of the other temperatures tested.

The effect of temperature on the rate of an enzyme-controlled reaction

> **Example**
>
> The experiment above **ONLY** gives information about this particular enzyme-controlled reaction. You can't conclude that **all** enzyme-controlled reactions happen faster at a particular temperature — only this one. And you can't say for sure that doing the experiment at, say, a different constant pressure, wouldn't give a different optimum temperature.

You Need to Look **Critically** at Your Results

There are a few bits of lingo that you need to **understand**. They'll be useful when you're evaluating how convincing your results are.

1) **Valid results** — Valid results answer the original question. For example, if you haven't **controlled all the variables** your results won't be valid, because you won't be testing just the thing you wanted to.

2) **Accurate** — Accurate results are those that are **really close** to the **true** answer.

3) **Precise results** — These are results taken using **sensitive instruments** that measure in **small increments**, e.g. pH measured with a meter (pH 7.692) will be **more precise** than pH measured with paper (pH 7).

   > It's possible for results to be precise **but not** accurate, e.g. a balance that weighs to 1/1000 th of a gram will give precise results but if it's not **calibrated** properly the results won't be accurate.

   You may have to calculate the percentage error of a measurement.
   E.g. if a balance is calibrated to within 0.1 g, and you measure a mass as 4 g, then the percentage error is: $(0.1 \div 4) \times 100 = 2.5\%$. Using a larger quantity reduces the percentage error. E.g. a mass of 40 g has a percentage error of: $(0.1 \div 40) \times 100 = 0.25\%$.

4) **Reliable results** — **Reliable** means the results can be **consistently reproduced** in independent experiments. And if the results are reproducible they're more likely to be **true**. If the data isn't reliable for whatever reason you **can't draw** a valid **conclusion**.

   For experiments, the **more repeats** you do, the **more reliable** the data. If you get the **same result** twice, it could be the correct answer. But if you get the same result **20 times**, it'd be much more reliable. And it'd be even more reliable if everyone in the class got about the same results using different apparatus.

Work **Safely** and **Ethically** — Don't Blow Up the Lab or Harm Small Animals

In any experiment you'll be expected to show that you've thought about the **risks and hazards**. It's generally a good thing to wear an apron and goggles, but you may need to take additional safety measures, depending on the experiment. For example, anything involving nasty gases will need to be done in a fume cupboard.

You need to make sure you're working **ethically** too. This is most important if there are other people or animals involved. You have to put their welfare first.

Answers

Unit 4: Section 1 — Kinetics and Equilibria

Page 5 — Rate Equations

1 a) Experiments 1 and 2: [E] doubles and the initial rate doubles(with [D] remaining constant) **[1 mark]**. So it's 1st order with respect to [E] **[1 mark]**.
   Experiments 1 and 3: [E] and [D] both halve, and the initial rate halves **[1 mark]**. Halving [E] alone would halve the rate, so changing [D] cannot affect the rate **[1 mark]**.
   The reaction is 0 order with respect to [D] **[1 mark]**.
   Always explain your reasoning carefully — state which concentrations are constant and which are changing.
 b) rate = k[E] **[1 mark]**
 c) The value of the rate constant, k, will increase **[1 mark]**.

Page 7 — More on Rates and Rate Equations

1 H^+ is acting as a catalyst **[1 mark]**. You know this because it is not one of the reactants in the chemical equation **[1 mark]**, but it does affect the rate of reaction/appear in the rate equation **[1 mark]**.

2 a) rate = $k[H_2][ICl]$ **[1 mark]**
 b) (i) One molecule of H_2 and one molecule of ICl (or something derived from these molecules) **[1 mark]**. If the molecule is in the rate equation, it must be in the rate-determining step **[1 mark]**. The orders of the reaction tell you how many molecules of each reactant are in the rate-determining step **[1 mark]**.
   (ii) Incorrect **[1 mark]**. H_2 and ICl are both in the rate equation, so they must both be in the rate-determining step OR the order of the reaction with respect to ICl is 1, so there must be only one molecule of ICl in the rate-determining step **[1 mark]**.

3 a) Rate = $k[NO]^2[H_2]$ **[1 mark]**
 b) (i) $0.00267 = k \times 0.004^2 \times 0.002$ **[1 mark]** $\Rightarrow k = 8.34 \times 10^4$
   Units: $k = moldm^{-3}s^{-1}/[(moldm^{-3})^2 \times (moldm^{-3})]$
   $= dm^6mol^{-2}s^{-1}$.
   $k = 8.34 \times 10^4\ dm^6mol^{-2}s^{-1}$
   [1 mark for correct value of k, 1 mark for units].
   (ii) It would decrease **[1 mark]**.
   If the temperature decreases, the rate decreases too.
   A lower rate means a lower rate constant.

Page 10 — The Equilibrium Constant

1 $K_c = \dfrac{[H_2][I_2]}{[HI]^2}$ **[1 mark]**
 At equilibrium, $[H_2] = [I_2]$ **[1 mark]**
 $\Rightarrow [HI]^2 = \dfrac{[H_2][I_2]}{K_c} = \dfrac{0.77 \times 0.77}{0.02} = 29.6$ **[1 mark]**
 $\Rightarrow [HI] = \sqrt{29.6} = 5.4\ moldm^{-3}$ **[1 mark]**

2 a) (i) $mass/M_r = 42.5/46 = 0.92$ **[1 mark]**
   (ii) moles of $O_2 = mass/M_r = 14.1/32 = 0.44$ **[1 mark]**
   moles of $NO = 2 \times$ moles of $O_2 = 0.88$ **[1 mark]**
   moles of $NO_2 = 0.92 - 0.88 = 0.04$ **[1 mark]**
 b) Concentration of $O_2 = 0.44 \div 22.8 = 0.019\ moldm^{-3}$
   Concentration of $NO = 0.88 \div 22.8 = 0.039\ moldm^{-3}$
   Concentration of $NO_2 = 0.04 \div 22.8 = 1.75 \times 10^{-3}\ moldm^{-3}$ **[1 mark]**
   $K_c = \dfrac{[NO]^2[O_2]}{[NO_2]^2}$ **[1 mark]**
   $\Rightarrow K_c = \dfrac{0.039^2 \times 0.019}{(1.75 \times 10^{-3})^2}$ **[1 mark]** $= 9.4$ **[1 mark]** $moldm^{-3}$ **[1 mark]**
   (Units $= (moldm^{-3})^2 \times (moldm^{-3})/(moldm^{-3})^2 = moldm^{-3})$

3 a) $K_c = \dfrac{[CH_3COO^-][H^+]}{[CH_3COOH]}$ **[1 mark]**
 b) Increasing the concentration of CH_3COOH will have no effect on the value of K_c **[1 mark]**.
   K_c is fixed at a given temperature. Changing the concentration of a reactant will change the concentrations of the products, but it won't change K_c.

c) The equilibrium position will move to the right OR to the products OR forward reaction will increase **[1 mark]**.
   The forward reaction is endothermic, so the equilibrium moves to the right to absorb the extra heat **[1 mark]**.
d) The value of K_c will increase **[1 mark]**.

Page 13 — Acids, Bases and pH

1 a) (i) A proton donor **[1 mark]**
   (ii) A proton acceptor **[1 mark]**
 b) (i) $HSO_4^- \rightarrow H^+ + SO_4^{2-}$ **[1 mark]**
   (ii) $HSO_4^- + H^+ \rightarrow H_2SO_4$ **[1 mark]**
2 Weak acids dissociate (or ionise) a small amount **[1 mark]** to produce hydrogen ions (or protons) **[1 mark]**.
   $HCN \rightleftharpoons H^+ + CN^-$ or $HCN + H_2O \rightleftharpoons H_3O^+ + CN^-$
   [1 mark for correct formulas, 1 mark for equilibrium sign.]
3 a) A monoprotic acid means that each molecule of acid will release one proton when it dissociates OR each mole of acid will produce one mole of protons when it dissociates **[1 mark]**.
 b) $[H^+] = 10^{-pH} = 10^{-0.55}$ **[1 mark]** $= 0.28\ moldm^{-3}$ **[1 mark]**.
   A strong acid will ionise fully in solution — so $[H^+] = [Acid]$.
   That's why the question tells you that HNO_3 is a strong acid.
4 $[NaOH] = [OH^-] = 0.125\ moldm^{-3}$ **[1 mark]**.
   $[H^+] = \dfrac{K_w}{[OH^-]} = \dfrac{1 \times 10^{-14}}{0.125} = 8 \times 10^{-14}\ moldm^{-3}$ **[1 mark]**.
   $pH = -\log_{10}[H^+] = -\log_{10}(8 \times 10^{-14}) = 13.1$ **[1 mark]**.
   A strong base ionises fully in solution too.
5 a) In pure water $[H^+] = [OH^-]$
   So $K_w = [H^+][H^+] = [H^+]^2$ **[1 mark]**.
   $[H^+] = \sqrt{K_w} = \sqrt{(1.47 \times 10^{-14})} = 1.21 \times 10^{-7}\ moldm^{-3}$ **[1 mark]**.
 b) $pH = -\log_{10}[H^+] = -\log_{10}(1.21 \times 10^{-7}) = 6.92$ **[1 mark]**.

Page 15 — More pH Calculations

1 a) $K_a = \dfrac{[H^+][A^-]}{[HA]}$ **[1 mark]**
 b) $K_a = \dfrac{[H^+]^2}{[HA]}$ $\Rightarrow$ [HA] is 0.280 $moldm^{-3}$ because very few HA will dissociate **[1 mark]**.
   $[H^+] = \sqrt{(5.60 \times 10^{-4}) \times 0.280} = 0.0125\ moldm^{-3}$ **[1 mark]**
   $pH = -\log_{10}[H^+] = -\log_{10}(0.0125) = 1.90$ **[1 mark]**

2 a) $[H^+] = 10^{-2.65}$ **[1 mark]** $= 2.24 \times 10^{-3}\ moldm^{-3}$
   $K_a = \dfrac{[H^+]^2}{[HX]}$ **[1 mark]** $= \dfrac{(2.24 \times 10^{-3})^2}{0.15}$
   $= 3.34 \times 10^{-5}$ **[1 mark]** $moldm^{-3}$ **[1 mark]**
 b) $pK_a = -\log_{10}K_a = -\log_{10}(3.34 \times 10^{-5}) = 4.48$ **[1 mark]**

3 a) $K_a = \dfrac{[H^+]^2}{[HCN]}$ or $\dfrac{[H^+][CN^-]}{[HCN]}$ **[1 mark]**
 b) $[H^+] = 10^{-4.15}$ **[1 mark]** $= 7.08 \times 10^{-5}\ moldm^{-3}$
   $K_a = \dfrac{[H^+]^2}{[HCN]}$ $\Rightarrow$ $[HCN] = \dfrac{[H^+]^2}{K_a}$ **[1 mark]**
   $[HCN] = \dfrac{[H^+]^2}{K_a} = \dfrac{(7.08 \times 10^{-5})^2}{4.9 \times 10^{-10}} = 10.23\ moldm^{-3}$ **[1 mark]**
 c) $pK_a = -\log_{10}K_a = -\log_{10}(6.17 \times 10^{-10}) = 9.31$ **[1 mark]**

4 $K_a = 10^{-pKa} = 10^{-3.16} = 6.92 \times 10^{-4}\ moldm^{-3}$ **[1 mark]**
   $K_a = \dfrac{[H^+]^2}{[HF]}$ $\Rightarrow$ $[H^+]^2 = K_a[HF]$ **[1 mark]**
   $K_a[HF] = (6.92 \times 10^{-4})(0.5) = 3.46 \times 10^{-4}\ moldm^{-3}$ **[1 mark]**
   $[H^+] = \sqrt{[H^+]^2} = \sqrt{(3.46 \times 10^{-4})} = 1.86 \times 10^{-2}\ moldm^{-3}$ **[1 mark]**
   $pH = -\log_{10}[H^+] = -\log_{10}(1.86 \times 10^{-2}) = 1.73$ **[1 mark]**

Answers

Page 17 — pH Curves, Titrations and Indicators

1 a) Any strong monoprotic acid, e.g. HCl, HNO₃ *[1 mark]*
Any strong alkali, e.g. NaOH, KOH *[1 mark]*
The shape tells you that this is a strong acid/strong base titration curve.
b) Any indicator that changes colour between pH 3 and pH 11, e.g. methyl orange, phenolphthalein *[1 mark]*.

2 a)

[1 mark for general shape correct,
1 mark for approximate start and finish pHs correct]
b) pH 7 *[1 mark]*

3 a) Y *[1 mark]*
b) NaOH$_{(aq)}$ + CH₃COOH$_{(aq)}$ → CH₃COONa$_{(aq)}$ *[1 mark]* + H₂O$_{(l)}$
[1 mark for correctly balanced equation]
c) Any indicator that changes colour between pH 7 and pH 12, e.g. phenolphthalein, cresolphthalein, thymolphthalein *[1 mark]*.
This indicator is suitable because it changes colour over the vertical part of the pH curve OR it will change colour at the equivalence point/end point of the titration *[1 mark]*.

Page 19 — Titration Calculations

1 a) HCl$_{(aq)}$ + NaOH$_{(aq)}$ → NaCl$_{(aq)}$ + H₂O$_{(l)}$ *[1 mark]*
b) i) 25.6 cm³ *[1 mark]*

ii) Moles NaOH = $\frac{0.1 \times 25.6}{1000}$ *[1 mark]* = 2.56 × 10⁻³ *[1 mark]*

c) Concentration HCl = $\frac{(2.56 \times 10^{-3}) \times 1000}{25}$ *[1 mark]*
= 0.1024 moldm⁻³ *[1 mark]*

2 a) H₂SO₄$_{(aq)}$ + 2NaOH$_{(aq)}$ → Na₂SO₄$_{(aq)}$ + 2H₂O$_{(l)}$ *[1 mark]*

b) i) Moles NaOH = $\frac{0.1 \times 35.65}{1000}$ *[1 mark]* = 3.565 × 10⁻³ *[1 mark]*
ii) Moles H₂SO₄ = Moles NaOH ÷ 2 = 1.78 × 10⁻³ *[1 mark]*

iii) Concentration H₂SO₄ = $\frac{(1.78 \times 10^{-3}) \times 1000}{25}$ *[1 mark]*
= 0.07 moldm⁻³ *[1 mark]*

3 Equation: HCl$_{(aq)}$ + NaOH$_{(aq)}$ → NaCl$_{(aq)}$ + H₂O$_{(l)}$ *[1 mark]*

Moles NaOH = $\frac{0.25 \times 10}{1000}$ *[1 mark]* = 2.5 × 10⁻³ *[1 mark]*
Moles HCl = Moles NaOH = 2.5 × 10⁻³ *[1 mark]*

Volume HCl = $\frac{(2.5 \times 10^{-3}) \times 1000}{0.1}$ *[1 mark]* = 25 cm³ *[1 mark]*.

Page 21 — Buffer Action

1 a) $K_a = \frac{[C_6H_5COO^-][H^+]}{[C_6H_5COOH]}$ *[1 mark]*

⇒ [H⁺] = 6.4 × 10⁻⁵ × $\frac{0.40}{0.20}$ = 1.28 × 10⁻⁴ moldm⁻³ *[1 mark]*

pH = −log₁₀ 1.28 × 10⁻⁴ = 3.9 *[1 mark]*
b) C₆H₅COOH ⇌ H⁺ + C₆H₅COO⁻ *[1 mark]*
Adding H₂SO₄ increases the concentration of H⁺ *[1 mark]*.
The equilibrium shifts left to reduce the concentration of H⁺, so the pH will only change very slightly *[1 mark]*.

2 a) CH₃(CH₂)₂COOH ⇌ H⁺ + CH₃(CH₂)₂COO⁻ *[1 mark]*
b) [CH₃(CH₂)₂COOH] = [CH₃(CH₂)₂COO⁻],
so [CH₃(CH₂)₂COOH] ÷ [CH₃(CH₂)₂COO⁻] = 1 *[1 mark]*
and K_a = [H⁺]. pH = −log₁₀ 1.5 × 10⁻⁵ *[1 mark]* = 4.8 *[1 mark]*
If the concentrations of the weak acid and the salt of the weak acid are equal, they cancel from the K_a expression and the buffer pH = pK_a.

Unit 4: Section 2 — Basic Organic Chemistry & Isomersim

Page 23 — Naming Organic Compounds

1 a) 1,4-dibromobutane *[1 mark]*.
b) 2,3-dibromobutane *[1 mark]*.
c) CH₂=CH–CH=CH₂ OR [structure] *[1 mark]*.
Buta-1,3-diene OR 1,3-butadiene *[1 mark]*.

2 a) [structure] *[1 mark]*
Butan-2-ol *[1 mark]*.
As long as you've drawn one OH group on the second carbon along the chain, counting from either end, you've got butan-2-ol.
b) But-1-ene *[1 mark]*.
But-2-ene *[1 mark]*.

Page 25 — Formulas and Isomers

1 a) Any two from: pentan-1-ol, pentan-2-ol, pentan-3-ol *[1 mark for each]*.
b) E-pent-2-ene *[1 mark]*.
Z-pent-2-ene *[1 mark]*.
c) propene *[1 mark]*.
cyclopropane *[1 mark]*.

2 a) C₄H₁₀O *[1 mark]*.
b) C$_n$H$_{2n+2}$O *[1 mark]*.
c) C₁₀H₂₂O *[1 mark]*.

d) [structure] *[1 mark]*.

Page 27 — Optical Isomerism

1 a) The property of having stereoisomers, which are molecules with the same molecular formula and with their atoms arranged in the same way *[1 mark]*, but with a different orientation of the bonds in space *[1 mark]*.

b) [structures E and Z]
[1 mark for each correct structure, 1 mark for correct E/Z labels.]

c) (i) [structures]
[1 mark for each correctly drawn structure — they don't have to be orientated in the same way as in the diagram above, as long as the molecules are mirror images of each other.]
(ii) An asymmetric carbon/a chiral carbon/a carbon with four different groups attached *[1 mark]*.
(iii) Shine (monochromatic) plane-polarised light through a solution of the molecule *[1 mark]*. The enantiomers will rotate the light in opposite directions *[1 mark]*.

2 a) [structure] *[1 mark for chiral carbon clearly marked]*
The chiral carbon is the one with 4 different groups attached.
b) (i) A mixture of equal quantities of each enantiomer of an optically active compound *[1 mark]*.
(ii) Smaller doses needed/drug is more effective *[1 mark]*, fewer side-effects (because there's no D-DOPA enantiomer) *[1 mark]*.

Answers

Unit 4: Module 3 — Carbonyl Compounds

Page 29 — Aldehydes and Ketones

1 a) Propanal *[1 mark]*

[1 mark]

Propanone *[1 mark]*

[1 mark]

b) (i) Nucleophilic addition *[1 mark]*

(ii) From propanal,

[1 mark]

This product *[1 mark]* will be produced in a racemic mixture, because it's asymmetrical/contains a chiral carbon *[1 mark]*.

From propanone,

[1 mark]

c) (i) $CH_3CH_2CHO + 2[H] \rightarrow CH_3CH_2CH_2OH$ *[1 mark]*

(ii) e.g. $NaBH_4$ *[1 mark]* dissolved in water with methanol *[1 mark]*.

2 a) Butanal *[1 mark]* and butanone (or butan-2-one) *[1 mark]*

b) EITHER

Tollens' reagent (or silver nitrate dissolved in aqueous ammonia) *[1 mark]*

silver mirror with butanal *[1 mark]*

no reaction with butanone *[1 mark]*

OR

Fehling's or Benedict's solution (or copper II ions dissolved in NaOH or Na_2CO_3) *[1 mark]*

brick-red precipitate with butanal *[1 mark]*

no reaction with butanone *[1 mark]*

c) butanoic acid *[1 mark]*

Page 31 — Carboxylic Acids and Esters

1 a) $2CH_3COOH_{(aq)} + Na_2CO_{3(s)} \rightarrow 2CH_3COONa_{(aq)} + H_2O_{(l)} + CO_{2(g)}$

[1 mark for CH_3COONa, 1 mark for CO_2, and 1 mark for correctly balancing the equation.]

b) methanol *[1 mark]*, esterification (or condensation) *[1 mark]*.

Substance X is a carboxylic acid (ethanoic acid) and substance Y is an ester (methyl ethanoate).

2 a)

[1 mark]

b) Flavouring OR a perfume OR a plasticiser *[1 mark]*

3 a) $CH_3COOH + CH_3CH(CH_3)CH_2CH_2OH \rightarrow$
$CH_3COOCH_2CH_2CH(CH_3)CH_3 + H_2O$ *[1 mark]*

b) ethanoic acid *[1 mark]*

c) Heat OR warm OR reflux *[1 mark]* and (concentrated sulfuric) acid catalyst *[1 mark]*.

Page 33 — More on Esters

1 a) 2-methylpropyl ethanoate *[1 mark]*

b) Ethanoic acid *[1 mark]*

[1 mark]

2-methylpropan-1-ol *[1 mark]*

[1 mark]

This is acid hydrolysis *[1 mark]*

c) With sodium hydroxide, sodium ethanoate is produced, but in the reaction in part (b), ethanoic acid is produced *[1 mark]*.

2 a)

[1 mark]

b) $CH_3(CH_2)_7CH=CH(CH_2)_7COONa + H^+ \rightarrow$
$CH_3(CH_2)_7CH=CH(CH_2)_7COOH + Na^+$ *[1 mark]*

c) Shake with bromine water *[1 mark]*. It will turn colourless with oleic acid solution (due to C=C), but not with $CH_3(CH_2)_{16}COOH$ *[1 mark]*. You might never have heard of oleic acid before, never mind learned a test for it. But you're told it's got a double bond, and you should know how to test for one of them.

Page 35 — Acyl Chlorides

1 a) Ethanoyl chloride:
$CH_3COCl + CH_3OH \rightarrow CH_3COOCH_3 + HCl$ *[1 mark]*
Ethanoic anhydride:
$(CH_3CO)_2O + CH_3OH \rightarrow CH_3COOCH_3 + CH_3COOH$ *[1 mark]*
ethyl methanoate *[1 mark]*

b) Vigorous reaction OR (HCl) gas/fumes produced *[1 mark]*

c) Irreversible reaction OR faster reaction *[1 mark]*

2 a) $CH_3COCl + CH_3CH_2NH_2 \rightarrow CH_3CONHCH_2CH_3 + HCl$
[1 mark for correct reactants, 1 mark for correct products.]
N-ethylethanamide *[1 mark]*

b)

[1 mark for each curly arrow on first diagram.]
[1 mark for all 3 curly arrows on second and third diagrams.]
[1 mark for correct structures.]

Unit 4: Section 4 — More Organic Chemistry

Page 38 — Aromatic Compounds

1 The Kekulé model suggests that benzene has 3 C=C bonds. If this was true, the enthalpy change for benzene + $3H_2$ should be approximately $3 \times -120 = -360$ kJ mol^{-1} *[1 mark]*. The actual value of -208 kJ mol^{-1} means that the reaction is much less exothermic than this, so the Kekulé model does not fit the data *[1 mark]*.

2 a) Conditions: dry ether, reflux *[1 mark]*

b)

[1 mark]

c)

[1 mark]

d) For example, the aluminium only has 6 electrons in its outer shell, or the aluminium has an incomplete outer shell *[1 mark]*.

Answers

3 a) A: nitrobenzene *[1 mark]*
   B + C: concentrated nitric acid *[1 mark]* and concentrated sulfuric acid *[1 mark]*
   D: warm, not more than 55 °C *[1 mark]*
   When you're asked to name a compound, write the name, not the formula.

b) See page 38 for the mechanism.
   [1 mark for each of the three steps.]

c) $HNO_3 + H_2SO_4 \rightarrow H_2NO_3^+ + HSO_4^-$ *[1 mark]*
   $H_2NO_3^+ \rightarrow NO_2^+ + H_2O$ *[1 mark]*

Page 41 — Amines Mainly

1 a) It can accept protons/H+ ions, or it can donate a lone pair of electrons *[1 mark]*.

b) Methylamine is stronger, as the nitrogen lone pair is more available *[1 mark]* — the methyl group/CH_3 pushes electrons onto/increases electron density on the nitrogen *[1 mark]*. Phenylamine is weaker, as the nitrogen lone pair is less available *[1 mark]* — nitrogen's electron density is decreased as it's partially delocalised around the benzene ring *[1 mark]*.

2 a) $CH_3CH_2NH_2 + 3 CH_3Br \rightarrow CH_3CH_2(CH_3)_3N^+Br^- + 2 HBr$
   [1 mark] for correct structure/formula of the quaternary salt
   [1 mark] for correct balanced equation

b) An excess of CH_3Br *[1 mark]*.

c) For example, as a surfactant, in fabric conditioners or in hair products *[1 mark]*.

3 a) You get a mixture of primary, secondary and tertiary amines, and quaternary ammonium salts *[1 mark]*.

b) (i) $LiAlH_4$ and dry diethyl ether *[1 mark]*, followed by dilute acid *[1 mark]* OR reflux *[1 mark]* with sodium metal and ethanol *[1 mark]*.

   (ii) It's too expensive *[1 mark]*.

   (iii)Metal catalyst such as platinum or nickel *[1 mark]* and high temperature and pressure *[1 mark]*.

4 a) $CH_3CH_2NH_2 + CH_3CH_2Br \rightarrow (CH_3CH_2)_2NH + HBr$ *[1 mark]*
   The product is diethylamine *[1 mark]*

b) nucleophilic substitution *[1 mark]*

Then either:

OR

[1 mark for both curly arrows on first diagram.]
[1 mark for both curly arrows on second diagram.]
[1 mark for correct structures.]

Page 43 — Amino Acids and Proteins

1 a)

   [1 mark for the correct structure, and 1 mark for labelling the chiral carbon]

b) 2-aminobutanedioic acid *[1 mark]*
   (accept 2-amino-1,4-butanedioic acid)

2 a)

   [1 mark]

b)

   [1 mark]

3 a)

   [1 mark]

   You'll need a cool head for this one. Start with a 3-carbon chain and then add the groups — you start numbering the carbons from the one with the carboxyl group.

b) (i) Two amino acids joined together *[1 mark]* by a peptide/amide/–CONH– link *[1 mark]*.

   ii)

   [1 mark]

   [1 mark]

   The amino acids can join together in either order — that's why there are two dipeptides.

c) Hot aqueous 6 M hydrochloric acid/HCl *[1 mark]*, reflux for 24 hours *[1 mark]*.

Page 45 — Polymers

1 a) Polypropene *[1 mark]*

b) Addition polymerisation *[1 mark]*

c)

   [1 mark]

2 a) (i)

   [1 mark each]

   (ii) There are six carbon atoms in each monomer/reagent *[1 mark]*.
   Don't forget to count the carbons in the carboxyl groups too.

   (iii)Amide/peptide link *[1 mark]*

b) (i)

   or

   [1 mark]

   (ii) For each link formed, one small molecule (water) is eliminated *[1 mark]*.

Page 47 — More About Polymers

1 a) $CaCO_3$ *[1 mark]*
   $CaCO_3 + 2 HCl \rightarrow CO_2 + H_2O + CaCl_2$
   [1 mark] for correct reactants and products
   [1 mark] for balancing

b) CO_2 may contribute to global warming/greenhouse effect *[1 mark]*

2 a) (i) A — condensation polymer/polypeptide/protein/polyamide *[1 mark]*
   B — addition polymer *[1 mark]*

   (ii) A — 6-aminohexanoic acid *[1 mark]*
   B — propene *[1 mark]*

Answers

b) A [1 mark]
c) Advantages include: it is cheap and easy, it doesn't require waste plastics to be separated or sorted [1 mark].
Disadvantages include: it requires large areas of land, decomposing waste may release methane/greenhouse gases, leaks from landfill sites can contaminate water supplies [1 mark].

Unit 4: Section 5 — Synthesis and Analysis

Page 50 — Organic Synthesis and Analysis

1 a) Shake with bromine water [1 mark].
No reaction with A [1 mark].
Turns colourless with B [1 mark].
b) Tollens' reagent OR Fehling's/Benedict's solution [1 mark]
No reaction with C [1 mark].
Tollens' reagent gives a silver mirror with D OR Fehling's/Benedict's solution gives a brick red precipitate with D [1 mark].

2 a) propan-2-ol [1 mark]
b) % atom economy $= \dfrac{mass\ of\ desired\ product}{total\ mass\ of\ all\ reactants} \times 100$
M_r of Alcohol Q $(CH_3CH(OH)CH_3) = (12 \times 3) + (1 \times 8) + 16 = 60$
OR Mass of Alcohol Q $(CH_3CH(OH)CH_3) = 60\ g$ [1 mark]
Total M_r of all reactants $= M_r(CH_3CHClCH_3) + M_r(NaOH)$
$= 78.5 + 40 = 118.5$
OR Total mass of all reactants $= 78.5\ g + 40\ g = 118.5\ g$ [1 mark]
% atom economy $= (60 \div 118.5) \times 100 = 50.6$ [1 mark]
c) % yield $= \dfrac{actual\ yield}{theoretical\ yield} \times 100$
$M_r(CH_3CHClCH_3) = 78.5$, $M_r(CH_3CH(OH)CH_3) = 60$ [1 mark]
moles of $CH_3CHClCH_3 = $ mass $\div M_r = 39.25 \div 78.5 = 0.5$ [1 mark]
So 0.5 moles of $CH_3CH(OH)CH_3$ should be produced.
Mass of 0.5 moles of $CH_3CH(OH)CH_3 = 0.5 \times 60 = 30\ g$ [1 mark]
Percentage yield $= (24.9 \div 30) \times 100 = 83\%$ [1 mark]
d) $K_2Cr_2O_7$/potassium dichromate and H_2SO_4/sulfuric acid [1 mark]
Heat and reflux [1 mark]

3 Step 1: The methanol is refluxed [1 mark] with $K_2Cr_2O_7$ [1 mark] and sulfuric acid [1 mark] to form methanoic acid [1 mark].
Step 2: The methanoic acid is reacted under reflux [1 mark] with ethanol [1 mark] using an acid catalyst [1 mark].

4 Step 1: React propane with bromine [1 mark] in the presence of UV light [1 mark]. Bromine is toxic and corrosive [1 mark] so great care should be taken. Bromopropane is formed [1 mark].
Step 2: Bromopropane is then refluxed [1 mark] with sodium hydroxide solution [1 mark], again a corrosive substance so take care [1 mark], to form propanol [1 mark].

Page 53 — Mass Spectrometry

1 a) The M peak and the M+2 peak are the same height [1 mark]. This suggests the halogen is bromine [1 mark].
b) 136 and 138 [1 mark]
c) A has a mass of 29, so it's most likely to be $C_2H_5^+$ [1 mark].
B has a mass of 43, which is most likely to be $C_3H_7^+$ [1 mark].
C has a mass of 57, which is most likely to be $C_4H_9^+$ [1 mark].
Fragment B also has the same mass as a CHO group — but you know it's a haloalkane, and there are no CHO groups in haloalkanes.
d) You know it's a haloalkane and that the halogen is bromine. So if we take 79 (the A_r of one isotope of bromine) away from 136 (the M_r of the alkyl halide containing this bromine isotope), the alkyl bit must have a mass of 57 [1 mark].
All alkyl bits follow the general formula C_nH_{2n+1}.
n must be 4 to make this add up to 57. So the molecular formula is C_4H_9Br [1 mark]. To give fragment C, the bromine atom must be on an end carbon [1 mark].

H   H   H   H
| | | |
H—C—C—C—C—Br   [1 mark]
| | | |
H   H   H   H

Page 55 — NMR Spectroscopy

1 a)
4 peaks [1 mark]
This molecule has no symmetry — each carbon is joined to different groups and in a unique environment. So its ^{13}C NMR spectrum has four peaks.
b)
[1 mark]
3 peaks [1 mark]
One peak is for the red carbon (joined to $H_2ClCH(CH_3)_2$), another is for the blue carbon (joined to $H(CH_3)_2CH_2Cl$), and the third is for both green carbons, which are in the same environment (both joined to $H_3C(CH_3)HCH_2Cl$).
c)
[1 mark]
2 peaks [1 mark]
This molecule has three lines of symmetry — the three (blue) carbons with Cl atoms attached to them are all in the same environment, and the three (red) carbons that don't are all in the same environment. So its ^{13}C NMR spectrum has two peaks.

2 a)
[1 mark for each]
b)
OR propan-2-ol [1 mark]
There are only two peaks on the spectrum. So there must be exactly 2 different carbon environments in the isomer [1 mark].
c) Tetramethylsilane/TMS/$Si(CH_3)_4$ [1 mark]

Page 57 — More About NMR

1 a) A CH_2 group adjacent to a halogen OR $R-CH_2-Cl$ [1 mark].
You gotta read the question carefully — it tells you it's a haloalkane. So the group at 3.6 ppm can't have oxygen in it. It can't be halogen-CH_3 either, as this has 3 hydrogens in it.
b) A CH_3 group OR $R-CH_3$ [1 mark].
c) CH_2 added to CH_3 gives a mass of 29, so the halogen must be chlorine with a mass of 35.5 [1 mark]. So a likely structure is CH_3CH_2Cl [1 mark].
d) The quartet at 3.6 ppm is caused by 3 protons on the adjacent carbon [1 mark]. The n +1 rule tells you that 3 protons give $3 + 1 = 4$ peaks [1 mark].
Similarly the triplet at 1.3 ppm is due to 2 adjacent protons [1 mark] giving $2 + 1 = 3$ peaks [1 mark].

2 a) 3 [1 mark]
The three different hydrogen environments come from the H atoms that are attached to three different carbons in this molecule:

b) 3:2:3 [1 mark]
c) singlet, quartet, triplet [1 mark]

Answers

Page 60 — IR Spectroscopy and Chromatography

1 a) Gas liquid chromatography [1 mark]
   b) Different substances have different retention times [1 mark].
      The retention time of substances in the sample is compared against that for ethanol [1 mark].
   c) It is unreactive/does not react with the sample [1 mark].

2 a) A's due to an O–H group in a carboxylic acid [1 mark].
      B's due to a C=O as in an aldehyde, ketone, acid or ester [1 mark].
      C's due to a C–O as in an alcohol, ester or acid [1 mark].
      D's also due to a C–O as in an alcohol, ester or acid [1 mark].
   b) The spectrum suggests it's a carboxylic acid — it's got a COOH group [1 mark]. This group has a mass of 45, so the rest of the molecule has a mass of 29 (74 – 45), which is likely to be C_2H_5 [1 mark].
      So the molecule could be C_2H_5COOH — propanoic acid [1 mark].

3 a) i) $CH_3COOCH_2CH_3$ [1 mark]
      ii) CH_3COOH [1 mark]
      You can work out which carboxylic was used by looking at the number of carbons — the ester has 4 and ethanol has 2, so the carboxylic acid must also have 2 — i.e. it's ethanoic acid.
   b) Ethanoic acid [1 mark]. The peak is caused by C=O [1 mark]. This is present in carboxylic acids but not in alcohols [1 mark].
   c) i) The broad peak at around 2500 – 3750 cm^{-1} that is caused by the O–H bond in both ethanol [1 mark] and ethanoic acid [1 mark] would not be present in the spectrum of the ester [1 mark].
      ii) The peak in the region 1680 – 1800 cm^{-1} which is caused by the ethanoic acid would still be present in the ester [1 mark] because it also has a C=O group [1 mark]. The peak in the region 2800 – 3100 cm^{-1} would still be present [1 mark] because esters, alcohols and carboxylic acids all have C–H bonds [1 mark].

Unit 5: Section 1 — Thermodynamics

Page 63 — Lattice Enthalpies

1 a)

First ionisation energy of potassium (+419 $kJmol^{-1}$) $\Delta H4$
$K_{(g)} + Br_{(g)}$
$K^+_{(g)} + e^- + Br_{(g)}$
First electron affinity of bromine (–325 $kJmol^{-1}$) $\Delta H5$
Atomisation energy of potassium (+89 $kJmol^{-1}$) $\Delta H3$
$K_{(s)} + Br_{(g)}$
$K^+_{(g)} + Br^-_{(g)}$
Atomisation energy of bromine (+112 $kJmol^{-1}$) $\Delta H2$
$K_{(s)} + ½Br_{2(l)}$
Lattice enthalpy of potassium bromide $\Delta H6$
Enthalpy of formation of potassium bromide (–394 $kJmol^{-1}$) $\Delta H1$
$KBr_{(s)}$

[1 mark for left of cycle. 1 mark for right of cycle. 1 mark for formulas/state symbols. 1 mark for correct directions of arrows.]
   b) Lattice enthalpy, $\Delta H6 = -\Delta H5 - \Delta H4 - \Delta H3 - \Delta H2 + \Delta H1$
      $= -(-325) - (+419) - (+89) - (+112) + (-394)$ [1 mark]
      $= -689$ [1 mark] $kJmol^{-1}$ [1 mark]
      Award marks if calculation method matches cycle in part (a).

2 a) X: 2 × the atomisation enthalpy of chlorine
      OR the bond dissociation enthalpy of chlorine [1 mark]
      Y: the 2nd ionisation enthalpy of copper [1 mark]
      Z: 2 × the 1st electron affinity of chlorine [1 mark]
   b) The enthalpy of formation of copper(II) chloride [1 mark].
      The lattice enthalpy of copper(II) chloride [1 mark].
      The atomisation enthalpy of copper [1 mark].

Page 65 — Enthalpies of Solution

1 a)

$SrF_{2(s)}$ → (Enthalpy change of solution) → $Sr^{2+}_{(aq)} + 2F^-_{(aq)}$
lattice enthalpy of dissociation
$Sr^{2+}_{(g)} + 2F^-_{(g)}$
Enthalpy of hydration of $Sr^{2+}_{(g)}$
Enthalpy of hydration of $2F^-_{(g)}$

[1 mark for each of the 4 enthalpy changes labelled, 1 mark for a complete, correct cycle.]
Don't forget — you have to double the enthalpy of hydration for F⁻ because there are two in SrF_2.

---

   b) +2492 + (–1480) + (2 × –506) [1 mark] = 0 $kJmol^{-1}$ [1 mark]

2 By Hess's law:
   Enthalpy change of solution ($MgCl_{2(s)}$)
   = –lattice enthalpy of formation ($MgCl_{2(s)}$)
      + enthalpy of hydration ($Mg^{2+}_{(g)}$)
      + [2 × enthalpy of hydration ($Cl^-_{(g)}$)] [1 mark]
   = –(–2526) + (–1920) + [2 × (–364)] [1 mark]
   = 2526 – 1920 – 728 = –122 $kJmol^{-1}$ [1 mark]

3 a) Bonds broken   Bonds formed
      4 × C–H = 4 × 412 = 1648   2 × C=O = 2 × 743 = 1486
      2 × O=O = 2 × 496 = 992   4 × O–H = 4 × 463 = 1852 [1 mark]
      (1648 + 992) – (1486 + 1852) = –698 $kJmol^{-1}$ [1 mark]
      [1 mark for correct (negative) sign on final answer.]
   b) Some of the bond enthalpies used are averages [1 mark]. These may be different from the actual ones in the substances [1 mark]. OR enthalpy cycles use data for the actual compounds shown [1 mark]. Maximum 2 marks.

Page 67 — Entropy Change

1 a) Reaction is not likely to be spontaneous [1 mark] because there is a decrease in entropy [1 mark].
      Remember — more particles means more entropy.
      There's 1½ moles of reactants and only 1 mole of products (and this mole is a solid, which has a lower entropy than a gas).
   b) $\Delta S_{system} = 26.9 - (32.7 + 102.5)$ [1 mark]
      $= -108.3$ [1 mark] $JK^{-1}mol^{-1}$ [1 mark]

Page 69 — Free-Energy Change

1 a) (i) $\Delta S_{system} = 48 - 70 = -22$ $JK^{-1}mol^{-1}$ [1 mark]
      $\Delta S_{surroundings} = -(-6000)/250 = +24$ $JK^{-1}mol^{-1}$ [1 mark]
      $\Delta S_{total} = \Delta S_{system} + \Delta S_{surroundings} = -22 + 24 = +2$ $JK^{-1}mol^{-1}$ [1 mark]
      (ii) $\Delta S_{surroundings} = -(-6000)/300 = +20$ $JK^{-1}mol^{-1}$ [1 mark]
      $\Delta S_{total} = \Delta S_{system} + \Delta S_{surroundings} = -22 + 20 = -2$ $JK^{-1}mol^{-1}$ [1 mark]
   b) 250 K: $\Delta G = -6 \times 10^3 - 250 \times -22 = -500$.
      ΔG is negative so the reaction is feasible at 250 K [1 mark].
      At 300 K, $\Delta G = -6 \times 10^3 - 300 \times -22 = 600$
      ΔG is positive so the reaction is not feasible at 300 K [1 mark].

2 a) $\Delta G = 117 \times 10^3 - (550 \times 175) = +20\,750$ $Jmol^{-1}$ [1 mark].
      The value of ΔG is positive at 550K, so the reaction will not occur spontaneously at this temperature [1 mark].
   b) $T = \Delta H \div \Delta S_{system} = 117 \times 10^3 \div 175$ [1 mark] = 668.6 K [1 mark].

Unit 5: Section 2 — Period 3 and Redox Equilibria

Page 71 — Period 3 Elements and Oxides

1 a) SO_3 [1 mark], $SO_3 + H_2O \rightarrow H_2SO_4$ [1 mark]
   b) (i) Na_2O [1 mark], $Na_2O + H_2O \rightarrow 2NaOH$ [1 mark]
      (ii) Na_2O has a giant lattice structure [1 mark] with strong ionic bonds [1 mark], that take a lot of energy to break [1 mark].

2 a) $P_4 + 5O_2 \rightarrow P_4O_{10}$ or $4P + 5O_2 \rightarrow P_4O_{10}$ [1 mark]
   b) (i) $P_4O_{10} + 6H_2O \rightarrow 4H_3PO_4$ [1 mark]
      (ii) The solution is acidic, with a pH of 0-2 [1 mark].
   c) $P_4O_{10} + 12KOH \rightarrow 4K_3PO_4 + 6H_2O$ [1 mark]

Page 73 — Redox Equations

1 a) $Ti + (4 \times -1) = 0$, $Ti = +4$ [1 mark]
   b) $(2 \times V) + (5 \times -2) = 0$, $V = +5$ [1 mark]
   c) $Cr + (4 \times -2) = -2$, $Cr = +6$ [1 mark]
   d) $(2 \times Cr) + (2 \times -7) = -2$, $Cr = +6$ [1 mark]

2 $Cr_2O_7^{2-}{}_{(aq)} + 14H^+_{(aq)} + 6e^- \rightarrow 2Cr^{3+}_{(aq)} + 7H_2O_{(l)}$ [1 mark]
   $Zn_{(aq)} \rightarrow Zn^{2+}_{(aq)} + 2e^-$ [1 mark]

3 a) $2MnO_4^-{}_{(aq)} + 16H^+_{(aq)} + 10I^-_{(aq)} \rightarrow 2Mn^{2+}_{(aq)} + 8H_2O_{(l)} + 5I_{2(aq)}$
      [1 mark for correct reactants and products, 1 mark for correct balancing]
      You have to balance the number of electrons before you can combine the half-equations. And always double-check that your equation definitely balances. It's easy to slip up and throw away marks.
   b) Mn has been reduced [1 mark] from +7 to +2 [1 mark].
      I⁻ has been oxidised [1 mark] from –1 to 0 [1 mark].

Answers

c) *Reactive metals have a tendency to lose electrons, so are good reducing agents [1 mark].* I⁻ *is already in its reduced form [1 mark].*

Page 75 — Electrode Potentials

1 a) $Zn_{(s)} | Zn^{2+}_{(aq)} || Ag^+_{(aq)} | Ag_{(s)}$
   [1 mark for zinc on the left and silver on the right, 1 mark for the oxidised products in the middle.]

b) $+0.80 V - (-0.76 V) = 1.56 V$ *[1 mark]*

c) *The concentration of* Zn^{2+} *ions or* Ag^+ *ions was not 1.00 moldm⁻³ [1 mark]. The pressure wasn't 100 kPa [1 mark].*
   The difference can't be due to temperature, because it was standard during the experiment (25 °C is the same as 298 K).

d) $Zn_{(s)} + 2Ag^+_{(aq)} \rightarrow Zn^{2+}_{(aq)} + 2Ag_{(s)}$ *[1 mark]*

e) *The zinc half-cell. It has a more negative standard electrode potential/it's less electronegative [1 mark].*

Page 77 — Electrochemical Series

1 a) $Zn_{(s)} + Ni^{2+}_{(aq)} \rightleftharpoons Zn^{2+}_{(aq)} + Ni_{(s)}$ *[1 mark]*
   $E^\circ = (-0.25) - (-0.76) = +0.51 V$ *[1 mark]*

b) $2MnO_4^-{}_{(aq)} + 16H^+_{(aq)} + 5Sn^{2+}_{(aq)} \rightleftharpoons$
   $2Mn^{2+}_{(aq)} + 8H_2O_{(l)} + 5Sn^{4+}_{(aq)}$ *[1 mark]*
   $E^\circ = (+1.52) - (+0.15) = +1.37 V$ *[1 mark]*

c) *No reaction [1 mark]. Both reactants are in their oxidised form [1 mark].*

d) $Ag^+_{(aq)} + Fe^{2+}_{(aq)} \rightleftharpoons Ag_{(s)} + Fe^{3+}_{(aq)}$ *[1 mark]*
   $E^\circ = (+0.80) - (+0.77) = +0.03 V$ *[1 mark]*

2 a) (i) $Fe_{(s)} | Fe^{2+}_{(aq)} || O_{2(g)} | OH^-_{(aq)}$ *[1 mark]*
   (ii) $0.40 - (-0.44) = +0.84 V$ *[1 mark]*
   You should come out with a positive value when you calculate the e.m.f. of a cell — check you've done the subtraction the right way around if you get a negative value.

b) *The iron half-cell has a more negative electrode potential than the oxygen/water half-cell, so iron is oxidised [1 mark].*

Page 79 — Electrochemical Cells

1 a) $0.34 - (-2.38) = +2.72 V$ *[1 mark]*

b) $0.34 - (-0.76) = +1.10 V$ *[1 mark]*

2 a) (i) $O_2 + 4H^+ + 4e^- \rightarrow 2H_2O$ *[1 mark]*
   (ii) *From the reaction of hydrogen at the negative electrode [1 mark].*

b) *Advantages include: fuel cells don't need electrically recharging, the only waste product is water [1 mark].*
   Disadvantages include: hydrogen is highly flammable so is difficult to store or transport safely, electricity is needed to produce the raw materials [1 mark].

Unit 5: Section 3 — Transition Metals

Page 81 — Transition Metals — The Basics

1 a) $1s^2 2s^2 2p^6 3s^2 3p^6 3d^{10}$ *or* $[Ar]3d^{10}$ *[1 mark]*

b) *No, it doesn't [1 mark].* Cu^+ *ions have a full 3d subshell [1 mark].*

c) *copper(II) sulfate* $(CuSO_{4(aq)})$ *[1 mark].*

2 a) $+5$ *[1 mark]*

b) (i) $MnO_4^- + 8H^+ + 5e^- \rightarrow Mn^{2+} + 4H_2O$ *[1 mark]*
   (ii) $V^{3+} + 2H_2O \rightarrow VO_2^+ + 4H^+ + 2e^-$ *[1 mark]*

c) $2MnO_4^- + 5V^{3+} + 2H_2O \rightarrow 2Mn^{2+} + 5VO_2^+ + 4H^+$ *[1 mark for correct reactants and products, 1 mark for correct balancing]*
   Remember to check that the charges balance when you combine two half-equations, you'll often need to multiply everything in one of them.

Page 83 — Complex Ions

1 a) (i) *A species (atom, ion or molecule) that donates a lone pair of electrons to form a coordinate bond with a metal atom or ion [1 mark].* NH_3 *is a ligand in* $[Ag(NH_3)_2]^+$ *[1 mark].*
   (ii) *A covalent bond in which both electrons come from the same species [1 mark]. Both electrons come from a nitrogen [1 mark] in each coordinate bond in* $[Ag(NH_3)_2]^+$.
   (iii) *The number of coordinate bonds formed with the central metal atom or ion [1 mark]. In* $[Ag(NH_3)_2]^+$, *the coordination number is 2 because two* NH_3 *ligands are bonded to* Ag^+ *[1 mark].*

b) *Linear [1 mark]*

2 a) *Coordination number: 6 [1 mark] shape: octahedral [1 mark]*

b) *Coordination number: 4 [1 mark] shape: tetrahedral [1 mark] formula:* $[CuCl_4]^{2-}$ *[1 mark]*

c) *Cl⁻ ligands are larger than water ligands [1 mark], so only 4 Cl⁻ ligands can fit around the* Cu^{2+} *ion [1 mark].*

3 a) $[Co(H_2O)_6]^{2+} + 3NH_2CH_2CH_2NH_2$
   $\rightarrow [Co(NH_2CH_2CH_2NH_2)_3]^{2+} + 6H_2O$
   [1 mark for the correct formula of ethane-1,2-diamine, and 1 mark for the correct equation]

b)

   [1 mark for showing two bonds between the nitrogens on the ligand and the Co ion, and 1 mark for indicating clearly that they are coordinate bonds.]

Page 85 — Formation of Coloured Ions

1 a) *Energy is absorbed from visible light [1 mark] when electrons move from the ground state to a higher energy level [1 mark].*

b) *Change in oxidation state [1 mark], ligand [1 mark] or coordination number [1 mark].*

2 *Prepare a range of dilutions of known concentrations [1 mark]. Measure the absorbance of the solutions [1 mark]. Plot a graph of concentration versus absorbance [1 mark].*

3 a) ΔE *is the energy absorbed [1 mark] when an electron moves from the ground state to a higher energy level/excited state [1 mark]. OR* ΔE *is the difference between the ground state energy [1 mark] and the energy of an excited electron [1 mark].*

b) (i) Cu^+ *[Ar]* $3d^{10}$ *[1 mark]*
   (ii) Cu^{2+} *[Ar]* $3d^9$ *[1 mark]*

c) Cu^{2+} *[1 mark] because it has an incomplete d-subshell [1 mark].*

Page 87 — Variable Oxidation States

1 a) $Cr_2O_7^{2-} + 14H^+ + 6e^- \rightarrow 2Cr^{3+} + 7H_2O$ *[1 mark]*

b) (i) *The two half-equations are:*
   $Cr_2O_7^{2-} + 14H^+ + 16e^- \rightarrow 2Cr^{3+} 7H_2O$
   $CH_3CH_2OH \rightarrow CH_3CHO + 2H^+ + 2e^-$
   So the full equation is:
   $Cr_2O_7^{2-} + 3CH_3CH_2OH + 8H^+ \rightarrow 2Cr^{3+} + 3CH_3CHO + 7H_2O$
   [1 mark for correct reactants and products, 1 mark for correct balancing]
   Don't forget to balance half-equations by adding H_2O, H^+ and e^- — see page 73 for more.
   (ii) *orange → green [1 mark]*

c) (i) $SO_2 + 2H_2O \rightarrow SO_4^{2-} + 4H^+ + 2e^-$ *[1 mark]*
   (ii) $Cr_2O_7^{2-} + 3SO_2 + 2H^+ \rightarrow 2Cr^{3+} + 3SO_4^{2-} + H_2O$ *[1 mark]*
   For this one, you needed to triple everything in the half-equation from c(i) so that it has the same number of electrons as the half-equation in a).

2 a) $Cr^{3+}_{(aq)}$ *or* $[Cr(H_2O)_6]^{3+}$ *[1 mark]*

b) -1 *[1 mark]*

c) $2CrO_4^{2-} + H^+ \rightarrow Cr_2O_7^{2-} + OH^-$ *[1 mark]*
   orange [1 mark]

Answers

Page 89 — Titrations with Transition Metals

1 a) Moles of $Cr_2O_7^{2-}$ added $= \dfrac{0.0100 \times 29.40}{1000} = 2.94 \times 10^{-4}$

   [1 mark for the correct formula, 1 mark for the correct answer.]

   b) 6 moles of Fe^{2+} react with 1 moles of $Cr_2O_7^{2-}$
   So moles of Fe^{2+} reacted $= 2.94 \times 10^{-4} \times 6 = 1.76 \times 10^{-3}$ **[1 mark]**

   c) Mass of Fe $= A_r \times$ moles $= 55.8 \times 1.76 \times 10^{-3} = 0.0984$ g
   [1 mark for the correct formula, 1 mark for the correct answer.]

   d) % Fe $= \dfrac{0.0984}{0.100} \times 100 = 98.4\%$ **[1 mark]**

2 Moles of MnO_4^- added $= \dfrac{0.0200 \times 18.30}{1000} = 3.66 \times 10^{-4}$

   [1 mark for the correct formula, 1 mark for the correct answer.]
   5 moles of $C_2O_4^{2-}$ react with 2 moles of MnO_4^-

   so moles of $C_2O_4^{2-}$ added $= \dfrac{3.66 \times 10^{-4} \times 5}{2} = 9.15 \times 10^{-4}$

   [1 mark for the correct formula, 1 mark for the correct answer.]
   M_r of $Na_2C_2O_4 = (23 \times 2) + (12 \times 2) + (16 \times 4) = 134$ **[1 mark]**
   Mass of $Na_2C_2O_4 = M_r \times$ moles $= 134 \times 9.15 \times 10^{-4} = 0.123$ g
   [1 mark for the correct formula, 1 mark for the correct answer.]

3 Add dilute sulfuric acid to the iron(II) sulfate solution **[1 mark]**.
   Titrate with potassium manganate(VII) **[1 mark]**.
   The remaining Fe^{2+} will be oxidised to Fe^{3+} **[1 mark]**.
   Calculate the number of moles of potassium manganate(VII) that react and use this to calculate the number of moles of iron(II), and hence the concentration **[1 mark]**.

Page 92 — Uses of Transition Metals

1 a) Vanadium(V) is reduced **[1 mark]** to vanadium(IV)
   $V_2O_5 + SO_2 \rightarrow V_2O_4 + SO_3$ **[1 mark]**
   Vanadium(IV) is oxidised **[1 mark]** to vanadium(V)
   $V_2O_4 + \frac{1}{2}O_2 \rightarrow V_2O_5$ **[1 mark]**

   b) (i) impurities **[1 mark]** are adsorbed onto the surface of the catalyst **[1 mark]**.
      Example: lead in petrol poisons catalytic converter
         or: sulfur in hydrogen poisons the iron catalyst in the Haber Process **[1 mark]**
      (ii) Reduced efficiency **[1 mark]**, Increased cost **[1 mark]**

2 a) Homogeneous — reactants and products in the same phase **[1 mark]**
   Heterogeneous — reactants and products in different phases **[1 mark]**

   b) (i) homogeneous **[1 mark]**
      (ii)

   [1 mark for enthalpy level of products lower than that of reactants, 1 mark for uncatalysed reaction having the greater activation energy, 1 mark for a catalysed reaction curve with two humps.]

3 a) Aldehydes and ketones **[1 mark]**.
   b) silver mirror/precipitate **[1 mark]**
   c) (i) $[Ag(NH_3)_2]^+$ **[1 mark]**
      (ii) linear **[1 mark]**
      (iii) colourless **[1 mark]**

Unit 5: Section 4 — Inorganic Reactions

Page 95 — Metal-Aqua Ions

1 Fe^{3+} has a higher charge density than Fe^{2+} **[1 mark]**.
   This means Fe^{3+} polarises water molecules more **[1 mark]**, weakening the O-H bond more **[1 mark]** and making it more likely that H^+ ions are released into the solution **[1 mark]**.

2 A blue precipitate **[1 mark]** of copper hydroxide forms in the blue solution **[1 mark]** of copper sulfate. On addition of excess ammonia, the precipitate dissolves **[1 mark]** to give a deep blue solution **[1 mark]**.
   $[Cu(H_2O)_6]^{2+} + 2OH^- \rightleftharpoons Cu(H_2O)_4(OH)_2$ **[1 mark]** $+ 2H_2O$
   $Cu(H_2O)_4(OH)_2 + 4NH_3 \rightleftharpoons$
   $[Cu(NH_3)_4(H_2O)_2]^{2+}$ **[1 mark]** $+ 2H_2O + 2OH^-$
   [1 additional mark for each balanced equation.]

3 a) (i) $[Cr(H_2O)_6]^{3+}$ **[1 mark]**
      (ii) $Cr(H_2O)_3(OH)_3$ **[1 mark]**
      (iii) $[Cr(NH_3)_6]^{3+}$ **[1 mark]**
   b) $Cr(H_2O)_3(OH)_3 + 6NH_3 \rightarrow [Cr(NH_3)_6]^{3+} + 3H_2O + 3OH^-$ **[1 mark]**

4 a) (i) Formation of a brown precipitate **[1 mark]**
      (ii) Formation of a green precipitate **[1 mark]**
   b) $[Fe(H_2O)_6]^{2+}_{(aq)} + CO_3^{2-}_{(aq)} \rightarrow FeCO_{3(aq)} + 6H_2O_{(aq)}$ **[1 mark]**
   c) (i) Formation of a brown precipitate **[1 mark]**
      (ii) Fe^{2+} has been oxidised to Fe^{3+} by the oxygen in the air **[1 mark]**

Page 97 — Substitution Reactions

1 a) $[Cu(H_2O)_6]^{2+} + 4Cl^- \rightarrow CuCl_4^{2-}$ **[1 mark]** $+ 6H_2O$
   [1 mark for balanced equation.]
   $CuCl_4^{2-}$ is yellow (allow green, which is the colour you would see when you actually do the experiment) **[1 mark]**
   b) $[Cu(H_2O)_6]^{2+} + 3C_2O_4^{2-} \rightarrow [Cu(C_2O_4)_3]^{4-}$ **[1 mark]** $+ 6H_2O$
   [1 mark for balanced equation.]
   c) $Cu(H_2O)_4(OH)_2$ **[1 mark]**, blue **[1 mark]**

2 a) $[Fe(H_2O)_6]^{3+} + EDTA^{4-} \rightarrow [FeEDTA]^-$ **[1 mark]** $+ 6H_2O$
   [1 mark for balanced equation.]
   b) The formation of $[FeEDTA]^-$ results in an increase in entropy **[1 mark]**, because the number of particles increases **[1 mark]**.
   c) $Fe(H_2O)_3(OH)_3$ **[1 mark]**

3 a) $[Co(H_2O)_6]^{2+} + 6 NH_3 \rightarrow [Co(NH_3)_6]^{2+}$ **[1 mark]** $+ 6H_2O$
   [1 mark for balanced equation.]
   You can fit the same number of H_2O and NH_3 ligands around a Co^{2+} ion because they are a similar size.
   b) $[Co(H_2O)_6]^{2+} + 3NH_2CH_2CH_2NH_2 \rightarrow$
   $[Co(NH_2CH_2CH_2NH_2)_3]^{2+}$ **[1 mark]** $+ 6H_2O$
   [1 mark for balanced equation.]
   c) $[Co(H_2O)_6]^{2+} + 4Cl^- \rightarrow CoCl_4^{2-}$ **[1 mark]** $+ 6H_2O$
   [1 mark for balanced equation.]

Index

A

absorbance 84, 85
accuracy 100
acid anhydride 34
acid dissociation constant 14
acidic buffer 20, 21
acidity reactions 94
acids 11, 12, 16, 71, 93
activation energy 91
acyl chlorides 34, 35
acylium ions 52
addition polymers 44
alcohols 22, 23, 28, 30, 31, 32, 34, 49, 58
aldehydes 22, 28, 49, 58
aliphatic amines 39, 41
alkalis 16
alkanes 22
alkenes 22, 23, 44, 49
aluminium 71
amides 34, 41
amines 34, 39, 40
amino acids 42, 43
ammonia 34, 39, 40, 94, 96
amphoteric 42, 94
anti-clockwise rule 77
arenes 36, 37
aromatic amines 40
aromatic compounds 36, 37, 38, 49
aspirin 35
atom economy 50
autocatalysis 91

B

bases 11, 13, 39, 71, 93
basic buffer 20
batteries 78
Benedict's solution 28
benzene 36, 37, 38
bidentate ligands 83, 96
biodegradability 46, 47
biodiesel 33
blood 21, 83, 91
bond dissociation enthalpy 61
bond enthalpy 65
Born-Haber cycles 62
breaking bonds 65
bromine 49, 52
bromine solution 49
Brønsted-Lowry acids/bases 11, 93
buffers 20, 21
burette 16, 88

C

calibration graphs 85
carbocations 52
carbon chains 22, 32
carbon environments 55
carbon monoxide 91
carbon neutral 33
carbonates 30
carbonyl compounds
    28, 29, 30, 31, 32, 34, 35
carbonyl group 28, 41
carboxyhaemoglobin 91
carboxyl group 30
carboxylic acids 22, 28, 30, 31, 34, 41, 58
carrier gas 59
catalyst poisoning 90
catalysts 5, 6, 10, 40, 81, 90, 91
catalytic converter 90
cationic surfactants 39
cell potential 74, 75, 77, 78

chain isomers 24
charge density 94
chemical shift 54, 56
chiral molecules 26, 27, 42
chlorine 52
chromate(VI) ions 86
chromatography 42, 59
cisplatin 92
closed system 8
colorimeter 85
coloured ions 81, 84, 86, 95, 96
column chromatography 59
complex ion stability 96, 97
complex ions 81, 82, 93, 94, 95, 96, 97
compound ions 72
concentration 4, 5, 9, 10, 18, 85, 88
concentration-time graph 4, 5
conclusions 100
condensation polymers 43, 44
controlled experiments 3
coordinate bonds 82, 83, 93, 96
coordination number 82, 84, 96
correlation 99
covalent character 62
cycloalkanes 22

D

d orbitals 90
d-block elements 80
data handling 98, 99, 100
delocalised structure of benzene 36, 37
deuterated solvents 57
diamines 44
dicarboxylic acids 44, 45
dichromate(VI) ions 86, 88
diols 45
diprotic acids 12, 18, 19
disorder 66
displayed formula 24
dissociation 11, 12, 14
dissolving 64, 66
double bonds 23, 32, 44
dyes 38
dynamic equilibrium 8

E

e.m.f. 74, 78
E/Z isomerism 25
EDTA 83
electrochemical cells 74, 78, 79
electrochemical series 76
electrode potentials 74, 75, 76, 77
electron affinity 61, 62
electron pair acceptors 93
electron pair donors 93
electrophilic substitution 37, 38
empirical formula 24
enantiomers 26
end point 16, 88
endothermic reactions 10, 61, 64, 65, 66, 68
energy gap 84
energy levels 81, 84
enthalpy 37, 61
enthalpy change 61, 62, 64, 65, 68, 97
        of atomisation 61, 62
        of formation 61, 62
        of hydration 61, 64
        of solution 61, 64
enthalpy cycles 64
enthalpy profile 91
entropy 66, 67, 68, 69, 97
equilibrium 8, 9, 11, 14, 20, 86, 96, 97

equilibrium concentrations 8, 9
equilibrium constant 8, 9, 10, 11
equivalence point 16, 18
esters 30, 31, 32, 34, 58
ethane-1,2-diamine 83
ethanedioic acid 18
ethanoic anhydride 35
ethanol 58
ethyl ethanoate 58
evidence 2, 3
exothermic reactions 10, 61, 64, 65, 68
explosives 38
external circuit 74

F

fats 32
fatty acids 32, 33
feasibility 68, 69
Fehling's solution 28
first electron affinity 61, 62
first ionisation enthalpy 61, 62
first order reactions 4
fishy twist 39
flavourings 31
fragment ions 51, 52, 53
fragmentation pattern 51
free energy change 68, 69
frequency 54, 58, 84
Friedel-Crafts acylation 37
fuel cells 79
fuels 33
functional group isomers 24
functional groups 22, 24

G

gas-liquid chromatography (GLC) 59
general formula 24
glycerol 32
gradient of concentration-time graph 4, 5
graphs 99
group 2 elements 62

H

haemoglobin 83, 91
half-cell 74, 75
half-equations 73, 76, 77
haloalkanes 22, 40, 50
halogen carriers 37
Hess's Law 62, 64
heterogeneous catalysts 90
hexadentate 83
homogeneous catalysts 91
hydrogen bonds 43
hydrogen cyanide 29
hydrogen environments 56
hydrogen ion concentration 12
hydrogen peroxide 86, 87
hydrogen-oxygen fuel cell 79
hydrogencarbonates 30
hydrolysis 32, 43, 94
hydroxide precipitates 94, 96
hydroxonium ions 11
hydroxynitriles 29

I

indicators 16, 17
inert atmosphere 86
infrared spectroscopy 58
initial rate of reaction 4, 5
integration traces 57
iodide ions 91
ionic lattice 64

Index

ionic product of water 11, 13
ionisation enthalpy 61, 62
isomerism 24

K

K_a 14, 15, 21
K_c 8, 9, 10
Kekulé model 36, 37
ketones 28, 48, 49, 58
KEVLAR® 44
K_w 11, 13

L

lattice enthalpy 61, 62, 63, 64
Le Chatelier's principle 9, 20, 86
Lewis acids/bases 93
ligand exchange reactions 96, 97
ligands 82, 83, 84, 86, 96, 97
linear shape 82

M

M peak 51, 52
M+1 peak 51, 52
magnesium 70, 71
manganate(VII) ions 88
mass spectrometry 51, 52, 53
mass/charge ratio 51
mean bond enthalpies 65
melting points 70
metal carbonates 94
metal hydroxides 94
metal-aqua ions 93, 94
methyl orange 17
mobile phase 59
molecular formula 24
molecular ion peak 51
moles 18, 19, 61, 88, 89
monomers 44
monoprotic acids 12
Mr Clippy 51
multidentate ligands 83, 96, 97

N

n+1 rule 56
N-substituted amide 34
neutral solutions 12
neutralisation 16, 18, 71
nitration 38
nitriles 29, 40
NMR spectroscopy 54, 55, 56, 57
nomenclature 22, 31, 42
non-rechargeable cell 78
nuclear magnetic resonance 54
nucleophilic addition 29
nucleophilic addition-elimination 35
nylon 44

O

octahedral shape 82, 96
oils 32
optical isomers 26, 27, 42
orbitals 84
order of reaction 4, 5, 6
organic synthesis 48, 49
overall charge 82
oxidation 72, 73, 74, 76
oxidation state 72, 81, 82, 86, 90
oxidising agents 72, 86, 87, 88

P

paper chromatography 42
peptides 43
percentage yield 50
perfumes 31
period 3 70, 71
peroxodisulphate 91
pH 12, 13, 14, 15, 20, 21, 86
pH curve 16, 17, 18
pH meter 18
pH scale 12
phenolphthalein 17
phosphorus 71
physical state 66
pipette 16
pK_a 15
Planck's constant 84
plasticisers 31
platinum electrode 74
polarisation 94
polyamides 44
polyesters 44, 45
polymers 43, 44, 45, 46, 47
polypeptides 44
polystyrene head 46
position of equilibrium 9, 10, 20, 75
positional isomers 24
potassium dichromate(VI) 88
potassium manganate(VII) 88
practical skills 98, 99, 100
precipitates 94, 95
precision 100
pressure 9
primary alcohols 23, 28, 49
primary amines 39, 40
proteins 43
proton acceptors 11, 93
proton donors 11, 93

Q

quaternary ammonium salts 39, 40

R

racemates 26
rate constant (k) 4, 7
rate equations 4, 5, 6, 7
rate-determining step 6
reaction mechanisms
        6, 28, 29, 35, 37, 38, 40
reaction rate 4, 5, 6, 7
reactivity 70, 76
rechargeable cell 78
recycling 46, 47
redox reactions 72, 73, 74, 86, 88, 91
redox titrations 88
reducing agents 28, 40, 72, 86, 88
reduction 72, 73, 74, 76
reflected light 84
relative isotopic abundance 51
relative isotopic masses 51
relative molecular mass 51
reliability 100
retention time 59
reversible reactions 8, 9, 74
risk assessments 29

S

salts 20, 71
saturated fatty acids 32
scandium 80
second electron affinity 61, 62
second ionisation enthalpy 61, 62

second order reactions 4
secondary alcohols 23, 28, 49
secondary amines 39, 40
shampoo 21
silicon 71
silver complexes 82, 92
silver nitrate solution 50
skeletal formula 24
sodium 70, 71
sodium carbonate 94
solvents 31
splitting patterns 56
spontaneous reactions 66
square planar shape 82, 92
standard conditions 61, 75
standard electrode potential 75, 76, 77
standard hydrogen electrode 75
stationary phase 59
stereoisomerism 25
strong acids 11, 12, 16
strong bases 11, 13, 16
structural formula 24
structural isomers 24
sulfur 71
synthesis routes 48

T

tangent of a graph 4, 5
temperature 4, 8, 9, 10, 68, 69
tertiary alcohols 23, 49
tertiary amines 39, 40
Terylene (PET) 45
tetrahedral shape 82, 96
tetramethylsilane 54
thalidomide 27
theories 2, 3
titration 16, 17, 18, 19, 88
TMS 54
Tollens' reagent 28, 92
transition metals 80, 81, 84, 93

U

unidentate ligands 83, 96, 97
units of rate constant (k) 7
unsaturated fatty acids 32
unsaturation 49

V

validity 100
variable oxidation states 81
variables 98
visible light 84
voltage 74, 75
voltmeter 74
volume 18, 89

W

washing powder 21
waste plastics 46
water 11, 34
wavelength 58
weak acids 11, 14, 16, 20, 21, 30
weak bases 11, 16, 20
wise chemists of old 12

Z

zero order reactions 4
zinc 80, 86
zwitterions 42